# Growing Season

# *Nimrod International Journal*

# Growing Season

*Nimrod International Journal* IS INDEXED IN
HUMANITIES INTERNATIONAL COMPLETE

ISBN: 0-9794967-7-2 ISSN: 0029-053X
Volume 54, Number 2
Spring/Summer 2011

THE UNIVERSITY OF TULSA — TULSA, OKLAHOMA

*This issue of Nimrod is dedicated to*
*Manly Johnson,*
*longtime advisor and Poetry Editor,*
*1920 — 2010.*

## *Poetry Is Not Like That*

Comes stark naked
    in from the cold,
saunters up to the fire
    as if it owns the place,
settles down in your favorite chair.

You turn your head
    and—whoosh—it's gone.
Sometimes a lingering fragrance
    and a sense
that Spring is here to stay.

—M. J.

## Editorial Board

## Advisory Board

# Acknowledgements

This issue of *Nimrod* is funded by donations, subscriptions, and sales. *Nimrod* and The University of Tulsa acknowledge with gratitude the many individuals and organizations that support *Nimrod*'s publication, annual prize, and outreach programs: *Nimrod*'s Advisory and Editorial Boards; and *Nimrod*'s Angels, Benefactors, Donors, and Patrons.

| | |
|---|---|
| Angel ($1,000+) | Ellen Adelson, Margery Bird, Joan Flint, Stephani Franklin, Ruth K. Nelson, The John Steele Zink Foundation |
| Benefactor ($500+) | Cynthia Gustavson, The Jean & Judith Pape Adams Foundation, Bruce Kline, Donna O'Rourke & Tom Twomey, Lisa Ransom, Diane & James Seebass, Ann Daniel Stone, Randi & Fred Wightman, Joy Whitman, Jane Wiseman |
| Donor ($100+) | Harvey Blumenthal, Richard D. Bryan, Mary Cantrell & Jason Brimer, Katherine Coyle, Harry Cramton, Jackie & Mark Darrah, Ivy & Joe Dempsey, Kimberly Doenges, William Elson, Nancy & Ray Feldman, Sue & William Flynn, Sherri Goodall, Ann Graves, Ellen Hartman, Helen Jo Harwick, Nancy Hermann, Elizabeth & Sam Joyner, The Kerr Foundation, Marjorie & David Kroll, Lydia Kronfeld, Edwynne & George Krumme, Robert LaFortune, Mary & Robert Larson, Mary Lhevine & George Schnetzer, Roberta Marder, Geraldine McLoud, Melvin Moran, Rita Newman, Catherine Gammie Nielsen, Nancy & Tom Payne, Pamela Pearce, Katie & Ron Petrikin, Judy & Roger Randle Marcialyn & Bernard Robinowitz, Patricia Rohleder, Andrea Schlanger, Lisa & Joseph Schula, Margaret Schula, Joan Seay, Fran & Bruce Tibbetts, Dorothy & Michael Tramontana, Ann Watson, Melissa & Mark Weiss, Ruth Weston, Marlene & John Wetzel, Michelle & Clark Wiens, Penny Williams, Josephine & Thomas Winter, Mary Young & Joseph Gierek, Thomas Young Revocable Trust, Rachel Zebrowski |
| Patron ($50+) | Helen & M. E. Arnold, Margaret Audrain, Linda & Marc Frazier, Martha King-Clarke & Stephen Clarke, Maria Lyda, Samanthia & Andrew Marshall, Carolyn Sue Stees, Renata & Sven Treitel, Krista and John Waldron, Peter Walter, Martin Wing, Douglas Young |

# Table of Contents

FRANCINE RINGOLD

# *Editor's Note*
# *Growing Season*

Is there anything new that one can say about spring? Or, for that matter, about any growing season? (There is, after all, winter wheat, and late-bloomers, and forced growth.). Yet here they are, in this issue, poems and stories and an essay that illuminate the theme sometimes figuratively, sometimes literally, while still avoiding stereotype and platitude. They elicit the complexity and challenge implicit in the notion of growth, in the periodicity implied by the word season—season, a time of year, a measure of a life span, a spice for life. There are lessons, for example, in gardens, there are fields of knowledge yet to explore.

As with writers of old, for example, the eclogues of Virgil, Shakespeare's poetry and plays, the garland of lyric poets of today and yesterday, the writers in this issue are fascinated not only by the thing itself—willow tree, violet, rose, sedge—but the metaphors it provides to express the human condition — also various and layered and subject to time.

We peel away the petals of this issue, one by one, and find "cardinals who mate for life," but also Liz Kay's weeping spring, though spring is "*not* the season for weeping." For as she tells us in her next poem "Rite of Spring," the "seasons have forgotten their order." All is disjunction too in Marianne Taylor's poem, similarly named "Rites of Spring," where politics, terrorists, and marching old men enter the green world and the fragrant lilac becomes wild and "splits the morning air."

Yet this too is a "growing season" when we remember with Whitman that "nature is change," that all that grows is tangled and shifting. Poem after poem after story reminds us not just of intrusion upon the placid and positive, but that, if we are to be, as Walt says, "a comrade of weeds," free and as "unpruned" as Mary Gilliland's narrator, we must have room to grow, to imitate Chris Bullard's tall flannel-leaved mullein scattering yellow buds everywhere from this most humble weed.

Summer, of all the seasons, seems to be marked by nostalgia but relieved from sentimentality by exacting language. Kenneth O'Keefe's "lustrous summer," Clifford Browder's "thistle-drunk bees," "fused juices," and "tang and mystery" recreate the season and "the secret of joy." Meanwhile, Jennifer Anne Moses' remarkable story, "Angels of the Lake," conjures matings lost and won and evokes the stasis that nature ultimately rejects.

Inevitably, there are, in this issue, works that deal with death, with the Shakespearean "winter of our discontent," the season of mourning. As Peter Serchuk says, "December . . . the weather and the war bitter and getting worse. . . ." Yet each individual poem or story alludes also to a sense of growth, a kind of rebirth, and a faith that the "upside down world" will right itself in time. For Michelle Brittan, that growth involves holding onto "the weak tether of language." Even one word of her grandfather's ancient Dayak reconnects her to the world he valued. And the "iris, the lupine, the baby blue eyes . . . the Calypso orchids" pushing through "inhospitable soil" in Jacqueline Kudler's poem and Diana Woodcock's "Desert Ecology" are a "signal of redemption" after each "long bitter season." As Susanne Kort reminds us, "Dying we always are. But dead. What does that mean?" And, as for T. S. Eliot's "dyspeptic tone and the kvetching," Richard Agacinski admonishes: "You complain about a dead world, a waste land. It's April on earth, and the cup of the earth fills . . ."

It is possible to continue recounting the wonders of growth and recurrence in this issue — including the set of ekphrastic poems, recreating paintings so that the moment does not stop shining; the stories, like Kay Sloan's "Give Me You," and Nicholas Maistros' "Woman of the Year," growing into an awareness of the complexity of relationship — but my efforts would be superfluous.

There is, in front of you, waiting to be leafed through, the entire issue, in which "each piece of writing is a challenge to stasis, an assurance of growth." Someone else said that oft-quoted clause, I can't remember who. Perhaps, as Cory Brown says, in "that dreamlike season between summer and fall," it will come to me.

Juan Franco, photograph

## *Petals*

The wind rises
and sweeps white petals
from the tree
in our side lawn. They litter
the grass like tissues
we've wept in and crumpled.

But it's spring,
and not the season for weeping—
as if weeping had a season,
as if weeping ever
dropped its leaves,
or flowered.

# *Rite of Spring*

You and I make love
as if it's spring,
though there's frost all around,
and the lilies
have yet to interrupt.

Birds forego their formations.
No reason to fly
south now that the seasons
have forgotten
their order.

You clear
the leaves from the pond
and the water sits
crystalline, free
of algae and other life.

I can feel the iris
undulating
in the hard soil, the tulips
polishing their cups. Tell me
the words

to set things right.

## *Rites of Spring*

*Where's his mama?* asks David
as we bury a young raccoon found
nestled in oak roots like a kitten at nap.
Heartbeat missing, limbs stiffening,
spittle glinting like ice in the early sun.
His claws still soft, fur downy,
he is page twelve in *Baby Animals*.

My husband says *light no more fires*
despite the late chill. Starlings are nesting
in the chimney we'd forgotten to screen.
Soon those falling three floors to the clean-out
will need burying too. Featherless, transparent
knots of blue veins, we'll wrap them in hankies.
Our six-year-old to officiate with prayer and twig cross.

And this Memorial Day, still numb from towers
turned to ash, we watch our town parade, four sons
and I. Old men march, their faces stiff and grim.
*No candy showers at this one, kids.*
A world away a teen straps on a bomb,
while flags at our cemetery whip—
and a blast of wild lilac splits the morning air.

## Jonathan Greenhause

# *Far from Eden*

*The trouble with trees*, she says, the wilting leaves
leaving their seeds seeping into furrowed ground,
she says, *The trouble with trees*

*is their tangle of veins and seeds,*
*the limping latticework of their leaves*, she says,
*their treasure-trove of crisscrossing twigs*

*causing manifold mysteries amongst miraculous sheaths*
*of sheltering leaves*, she says,
mentioning the mystifying mazes of sundered stems,

the treasure-trove of wriggling worms inside
shining skin and broken bark of trunks, she says
*The trouble with trees is their tangle of leaves,*

urban spaces' negations devouring their ancient forms,
a memory in living cells of rural life
clinging to their razed and wilting leaves, she says

*The trouble with trees is they're an alternative offering,*
*an anti-industrial presence facing an ever-burgeoning barrage*
*of blossoming buildings*, the relics of groves

showing intransigence in their rollicking roots,
how they slip in subterranean soil to avoid easy extirpation,
she says *The trouble with trees are their leaves*

*recalling our fall from grace, our ever-present expulsion*
*from that perfect unseen garden left behind,*
so increasingly far from us to see.

# *In His Construction of Internal Rhyme*

He wakes and writes a sonnet on his palm,
penning it beneath the crystal tongue of the bathroom faucet.
    Two hours afterwards,
his arms are hammering verses on a parchment of cement,
surrounded by the lamentations of a Greek chorus
    all dressed in jeans and cumulous clouds of dust
infiltrating, crowding swollen lungs.
They sing in metered, syncopated lines despite the chill embrace
    of gray November's airs,
an aria tenaciously gripping the threads of every throat.

Men and women spin around steel cables placed
as they lift up towering edifices to this urban maze.
    He counts each iron couplet in iambic strokes,
his callused hands trembling and remote,
and his mind's left drifting like a feather in the asbestos
    of an unshaped, unseen world:
Crisp octaves, pauses, and crescendos
    carefully coat each tiered section
of versed construction he sets down.

A whistle ends the stanza of their day.
He leaves as leaves are tumbling in a shower of shaking trees
    exposing rows of boughs.
Amongst these structures worn, he climbs a tree,
his palms impressed with syllables and stresses
    of a sonnet's spinning, repetitive caresses.
He smiles, peering into their scrawling script:
His beginning, middle, and ending are all laid out within its curves,
    while all around him
fleeing geese pen sonnets of their own
    against the breeze.

## Carol V. Davis

# *Roots*

I keep returning
to the gnarly roots of things:

nuggets of words freed
from their appendages

In Russian
a verb depends on its prefix:

Choose carefully for with one
you can make it home on the

St Petersburg metro
before it halts at 1am to allow

the 500+ bridges to yawn open
so the hulking freighters can

slink into harbor
before the captain finishes the last dregs of vodka

Choose the other prefix and
you'll be gazing out of the rickety tram

that sighs at every turn of track
as it sways out of the city on a late fall afternoon

If you're lucky you'll make it out
before sundown—the perfect time to forage

for mushrooms in the very forest where
the partisans hid, bits of song escaping over the treetops

It is cold by California standards
I burrow elbow-deep in a cardboard box

grasping for that perfect
knot of bulb that promises a red tulip

come spring and so much more

# *The Art of the Stitch*

On the lid of a seventeenth-century box, Queen Esther pleads with open palms
to the King. She understood a woman's power, for on the back panel
Haman swings from scaffolding,

hardly a suitable subject for needlepoint.
Other chair cushions illustrate the scandalous tale of King Solomon
and the Queen of Sheba, shown in various stages of undress.

Peering through glass on the third floor of a brownstone museum,
I am drawn to a lone tree on a box made to hold a lady's toiletries,
the tree where Charles II hid from Cromwell. I remember the family pilgrimage

to Shropshire to view that oak. At eight I worried there were not enough leaves
to hide the king, as if I could have saved him or my own relatives
whose fate my parents discussed when I was supposed to be asleep.

Now I petition for help: Teach me the art of the stitch:
French knot, ladder stitch, double cross; to learn
from the pattern maker the necessity of choice;

to master the art of the knot and tie down the pieces;
to snip and discard mistakes.

Let me unearth gold thread and silk cord,
trace the tail of a partridge, give it substance,
then set the bird free.

## Mary Gilliland

# *Move Over, Lover*

I'm horny as a spreading honeysuckle
yet—can I say this without hurt?—I need
the space of your body not reading
through the newspapers, not caring how I'm

doing, not in the know that I am back
or forth. I need an unwound proverb,
pixels deleted from my screen, a sewing
project I can't baste, a curriculum

for life with assignments enough to send
me wayward. What I do there is compost
to sweeten new potatoes and snowpeas.

Flowers bloom on their own, oracles that
I can't question. Spring hatches flying
ants. A shrub unpruned needs room.

# *Mullein*

> Every object has its lesson, enclosing the suggestion of something else—and lately I sometimes think that all is concentrated for me in these hardy, yellow-flower'd weeds.
> —*Walt Whitman,* "Specimen Days"

Ten yards farther, the chair advances for the poet
of lilacs and of self and of self in lilacs
who wobbles toward sanity and health.
"Strength," he says, "is perhaps the last,
completest, highest beauty." He seeks
correspondences, correlatives, coincidences
in the undergrowth, as he once sought
companions in the bars along Broadway.
His pockets are as voluminous as bureaus
and contain new systems, lists of favorite trees,
titles for his next book. He recites the names
and ranks and home states of the "typical soldiers"
he nursed. Images crowd him, yet he is alone.
He exercises, each day staggering farther down the lane
until he reaches the inner course of Big Timber Creek,
that bearer of silt and carp, snakes and crayfish,
that nourisher of water lilies and the Calamus
where he wills strength to himself, wrestles with trees,
and bathes in the marl deposits of Crystal Spring.
He is a naked and scandalous bearded old man
as he muses on the identity of plants and praises
the inherency of natural objects existing apart
from men's perceptions, apart from preconceptions,
and all assumptions of order. As he increases
the length of his walks, he encounters mullein,
that humble flower, thriving on disturbed ground,
living where men live. He describes it as plentiful
in summer and growing everywhere in the fields.
He admires the dew on the broad, fleece-like leaves
and the stalks, seven or eight feet high. Farmers
regard it as mean and unworthy, but he is a comrade
to weeds: to the outsider, the unwanted, the ignored.

At intervals, over three years, he returns to the mullein
that serves him as a lesson and a sign. Its hardiness,
its persistence in the fields, its grand rise and unfolding
give him peace, as he recognizes, though half of himself
cannot be regained, that he can change. "Nature," he says,
"is change."

Kimberly Colantino, *Evening Shadows*, photograph

# *Chiller Pansies*

Your pansies died again today.
All June I've watched them scorch and fall
by noon, their faces folding down
to tissue-paper triangles.
I bring them back with water, words,
a pinch, but they are sick to death
of resurrection. You planted them
last fall, these "Chillers" guaranteed
to come again in spring. They returned
in April—you did not. You who said
*pick all you want, it just makes more!*
one day in 1963,
and I, a daughter raised on love
and miracles, believed it.

## *It Might Be Happiness*

It might be happiness that stops my mouth.
Let me keep silent all day like a monk.
Let me pray over a simple bowl of rice and milk.
Let me find the right word before I speak this time.
The others talk, when there is nothing left to say,
or sing, because the house feels lonely to them.
But even crickets pause and wait for a response
before they fill the room again with noise.
And birds, the cardinals, who mate for life,
light on the sill and tilt their heads like so,
and all around the yard there might be snow
or wind unsettling the stable world,
but each will listen for the other one
and then continue as if satisfied.

# *A Broken Abecedarius of How Things Might Be if the World Were Saved*

*Achoo!* at the beginning of a tale.
Beasts wandering in daylight, unafraid of being shot, even
Centaurs, who would not be drunk anymore if invited to your wedding.
A dragon or a dinosaur named
Ellen.
Flies who would go to the front screen door on command so you could
let them out.
Galumphing as the normal gait of soldiers.
Hazelnuts that fall one by one into the mouth of the Salmon of Wisdom who swims
beneath, until the time comes for her to be caught by a wizard's
apprentice and cooked over a slow fire until she has rendered up all the
wisdom remaining in her unsung parts. But
I digress. . . .

Intoxication once a day by the scent from white
Jasmine flowers tumbling over a garden wall, except for the
Keepers of Butterflies, who would need to remain sober.
Loping as an alternate choice (see G above).
More respect for Dame Love, who has thoughtfully abolished Reason.
Nearly all the children reaching the house in the middle of the forest, where they will be
temporarily changed into birds, and introduced to their hearts' desire by a very
Old bear, who knows all the tales with caves in them.
Pearls of music rolling around between the warm, uneven bricks, under the chairs.
Quiet
Regales of yellow leaves, and the musk of grapes.
Sisyphus released from duty but staying on as a volunteer on weekends when he has
Time off from being a taxi driver in New York, something he has always wanted to
try.
An upset
Victory by
Whim, who has finally convinced Steven Hawking that she is indeed the final black hole
into-which-and-from-which comes
Xanadu with its plazas and feasts, its gardens of endless endings for which we have all
secretly
Yearned—and to which we have spent the last million years
Zigging and Zagging (see G above) and where we will arrive this very
AFTERNOON.

## *When the sun shines on the window pane in spring*

. . . it becomes clear
spiders are not losing their hair,
but rather, sending unscripted valentines.

Today's unbirthday greeting spun to remind you
that sure as the sun will set,
you are getting older.

It's not words that make it bearable
so much as the swing of the silk,
the dancing in the frame.

From the collection of the Editor, photograph

# *When What Mattered Most Was Small*

Noon's sun had struck Grandfather's lawn a blow.
It shimmered like a rusting sheet of emerald,
While violent heat in warping wavelets coiled
From concrete walks where few would choose to go.
Cooled by the shaded porch, we watched the flow
Of traffic. Through that afternoon we counted
The types of tires on which each car was mounted.
The black and white walls (some we didn't know)
Were scored a point for either you or me.
Some years older at ten, I took the black-
Rimmed, so I kept winning each time to twenty.
That lustrous summer brought nothing to lack.
We, brothers, shared a wealth of daily small
Things; lucky then to think we had it all.

## Clifford Browder

# *Till Our Juices Fused*

I said to the summer,
"Because you tease me
With purple spires, white crosses, pink stars
Because you entice me
With bristling
Seed pods of mustard, the plop
Of turtles in scummed ponds
Digger wasps and thistle-drunk bees,
I shall spy you out and leave
My prints on your flesh,
I shall put you in my pocket."

Going at her
With bird, flower and insect books
Sun-tan goo and bug repellent
And rubber-soled boots
With thick lugs and expensive stitching,
I trampled her thousand grasses
Plumed and undulant
And sprawling
In deep meadow watched
As from the pouting orange lip
Of butter-and-eggs
Red ants crawled out.

"I have had the summer," I announced
Rubbing
My forearms tinged
With a ridged rash.

But the summer
Rasped and murmured,
Lured me to her thighs
Where among beetle orgies
And grubs eating spider eggs
I looted her berries,
Tramped down, broke her briars.

Yet as I came away
Hammered by the sun
Tired, sated
My ankles tingling
With red welts of mosquito bites
That would itch for days,
I sensed
She was mocking me.

"Whore!" I cried
And in a frenzy of hygienic rage
Scrubbed my skin, scraped my boots
Tore from my cuffs and buttonholes
Her seeds and burrs.

Days passed, a week.
Restless
I hatched an insight: "Maybe
She's a very great lady exuding
Not lewdness but life
A benign goddess
To be worshipfully espoused
To be reverenced."

Humbly I went back
To the hot smell of weeds
Blood-gorged ticks.
Reverence was out of the question.

"Can we not
Be reasonable?" I said
Amid heat prickles
And larvae wallowing
In gray rot.
"Can we not communicate
On a higher level?" I said
Fighting off her zooming minutiae
As the weedy, grass-tough goddess
Smothered me
In wild onion.

Dazed
I sank down, let her insects
Suck my sweat and blood
Till our juices fused
And we could taste each other's
Tang and mystery.

## *The Secret of Joy*

When I was twenty
I wanted to speak in tongues
Eat rare earths, piss green, write poems
To blast the pants off fuddyduddies
And launching
My whippy-tailed sperm
Into poignant and disconsolate virgins
Gladden them
And lapse gaga in a fit of rapture.
My life
Was a storm of jubilance,
Hot rubble of dream.

When I was forty
I walked soft, thought small
A master of accommodation
Threading my ephemera
Through the mesh of seasons,
The scratch and buzz of time
Enhancing my normal regularity
With good dentistry and vitamins,
Reasonable greed.
Fleshy ditherings
And lyric mayhem
Were not my cup of tea.

Now, at eighty, quickening
My fertile dust
With dark energy I seek
A sly florescence known to no botanist
And striding
Past voids and vortices
Commit myself
To the gods of laughter and chance.
Proof against
Handbills proclaiming
Madame Irma, psychic adviser
Computer repairs—cheap!
The Total Ecstasy Asian Massage Parlor
(*Se habla français*)
Piles
And the Second Coming,
I look
Beyond presumption
Beyond lucidity
Hoping to snatch the secret of joy
Nestled in the groin of silence, prepared
To scrape against rejection and survive
Armed
With wit, spite, cunning
And scum-green stamina
Raked up
From the feisty guts of the sea.

## *Angels of the Lake*

Six women died during that one year, all but one of cancer, and that one, Shelley Saltz, had had cancer years before. It was strange, five women, all with mailboxes jauntily announcing their family's presence on the North Road, houses that dotted the shore of the lake, summers spent picking wild blueberries and baking them into pies and pancakes, summers spent first with children and then with grandchildren, and then, as chemo, nausea and bone loss took hold, not at all.

The brightly colored mailboxes (Nedra Frye had personally painted hers yellow with uneven pink polka dots) remained, as did the houses on the shore, the sailboats, the battered canoes, the smell of rain, the collections of pinecones and children's drawings, but most of all—it goes without saying—what remained were the husbands. It took no one by surprise when, just a year after Ellen Trowbridge had died (ovarian cancer), her widower, Calvin, showed up in the wedding pages of *The New York Times* with a woman he'd apparently known for better than thirty years, though, according to the text that accompanied a photograph of a beaming, bald Calvin with his clearly crinkled and sun-dried bride, the two of them had never lived in the same city. The last of the families to have "discovered," as the summer people said, the beauty and quiet loveliness of Lake Lantern, the Trowbridges were considered to be somewhat on the flashy side, always improving their property, which wasn't modest to begin with. Hardly: where once a three-bedroom wood-shingled cottage had stood, there now loomed three large and handsome houses with enormous plateglass windows gazing west, as if posing for the cameras, with the lake lying majestically beneath. Just three years earlier, with Ellen bloated and shaking from endless treatments and talking about who she wanted to speak at her funeral, Calvin had put in a tennis court. Now he and his new wife—a Frenchwoman by birth who'd kept her name—could be seen batting the tennis ball around at all hours, sometimes to each other, other times in the company of other couples. It wasn't a problem: people were happy for Calvin. He'd been devoted to Ellen during the long years of her illness. Why shouldn't he re-marry, and if his new wife was younger than he was, what of it? At sixty-something, she was hardly a baby herself.

And God alone knew that Calvin deserved a little happiness, a little fun, before his own old age encroached, and the new wife (Susan? Suzanne?) was a sunny, friendly, sporty sort of person, happy to tell you about her own first marriage to an American she'd met during a college trip to the States, her childhood riding ponies in Normandy, and how in the end she knew she could never leave New York, where she and her first husband, a magazine publisher, had lived. "After forty years here, I am a New Yorker, no?" she said in her lovely accent. Calvin introduced her as "My beautiful wife."

Within a year of Calvin's marriage, Peter Saltz, Eric Zamboni, and Stu Levine had also shown up at various Lake gatherings—the Fourth of July Parade, the annual Football-Fun-Fundraiser for the high school (summer people versus year-rounders), the Five-K Race for the Fire department—with women of the more-or-less permanent-status sort: a retired school teacher with faded brown hair and freckled arms; a woman who owned an art gallery on Beacon Street; and, for Stu Levine, his grown children's former Hebrew tutor, an Israeli who'd lived in Washington, D.C., (where Stu still practiced law) for most of her adult life, connected first to the Embassy and then to the man who became her husband before disappearing, himself, into the jaw and maw of illness and death. What could you do? the remaining intact, somewhat younger couples asked themselves. No one was getting any younger and in the end...well, in the end, there was only one end, for all of them. The question wasn't how you were going to face your own death, or when you were going to die, but rather, how to live life as the remaining half of a marriage. Was there something in the water, they jokingly asked, thinking of those five women, all of them dead within the same one year. But the thought was quickly dismissed: the waters, if anything, were an elixir, a magical sweet pool of such fragrant clarity that plunging into it revived one's early sense of wonder. Still . . . it happened, and regularly: husbands left alone, without their wives; wives left without their husbands. What if? What if? Most of the women were quick to declare that, if they predeceased their own husbands, they'd hope and expect their husbands to re-marry and the sooner the better. They said things like: "You? Live alone? For how long—ten minutes?" And: "Honey, you still can't so much as locate the washing machine. What would you do? Invest in an endless supply of Jockey shorts?" The forty-

and fifty- and even sixty-something husbands were not, as a rule, as jocose as their wives, not so generous with their futures. They crossed their arms and said things like: "I wouldn't want you to be alone, either, but I also wouldn't want you to rush into anything."

The widower who held out the longest, and in fact didn't seem inclined to re-marry at all, was Donald Frye, which took everyone by surprise, because Donald Frye had been devoted, practically to the point of adoration, to Nedra. They'd had the kind of marriage that other people talk about in tones of wonder and envy. How did they do it? Never a cross word, never a dismissive glance, not so much as an impatient sigh ever passed between them. He'd stayed with her in the hospital, night after night, after her initial surgery; fixed her favorite foods and tempted her with homemade puddings and soups when her appetite was poor; and of course, it had been Donald, rather than a hired aide or someone from the hospice, who'd nursed her through her final illness, staying with her as her breathing became labored, and then shallow, and then indefinite, and then no more. He was devastated, of course. Lost weight. Moped around. Took long walks with the dogs. People said that he was going under, that his mourning was taking too long, and was too severe. Was it good for him to be on the Lake all alone—all alone in that house filled with family memorabilia and Nedra's faded sundresses? Then his grown daughters and their children and old friends started to visit, filling the ramshackle cottage with bustle and the smells of cooking, and bit by bit he resumed doing the things he loved to do. Once again he was seen paddling his canoe across the lake with one or the other of his mutts sitting in the keel; once more he showed up at picnics talking about books—he and Nedra both had been great readers—or the heron he'd seen fly over the cove. The worst of his grief behind him, it seemed obvious that he should, and would, marry again, particularly as, more than anyone else that anyone could think of, Donald Frye was exactly the kind of man—loving, dedicated, kind, generous—who would *want* to marry again. They'd been happy, Donald and Nedra, she with her bright colors and box of paints, he with his wistful longing for the freedom and grace of nature. He *knew* how to be married. He was a handsome man too, with beautiful curling silver hair and blue eyes. Women noticed and liked him. Why should he hold back? What was stopping him?

Even Tommy Tompkins remarried. Two and a half years after Calvin Trowbridge's photo appeared in the wedding pages of *The New York Times* with his French bride, Tommy Tompkins was spotted on the lake in a new speedboat, a white-blonde woman in a red dress by his side. Moreover, the woman—whose name, it was soon found out, was Ray—was appropriate in every way, a widow herself, and a grandmother several times over. Everyone was delighted for him, of course, but surprised, too, because Tommy Tompkins hadn't been very good to Debbie Tompkins, either before or after she'd been found to have an inoperable tumor in her left lung (and the irony, of course, was that she'd quit smoking years earlier), and it had always struck everyone that the man had never been made for marriage to begin with. With Debbie he'd been impatient, dismissive of her opinions, easily annoyed. Every now and again, when she said something that he found particularly irksome, he'd roll his eyes. If she made an offhand remark about the trouble in Bosnia or the rising cost of housing, he'd say "Deb gets all her ideas verbatim from NPR," or "My wife, the commentator." It was embarrassing, but Debbie didn't seem to mind, or rather, if she did mind (as people suspected) she'd long since learned to hide her feelings. But that wasn't the worst of Tommy's sins in the marital department. There were stories that went around about him and, though stories were only stories, certain townspeople—Doug Smolers, for one—had seen him, always in the off-season, with a woman with long dark hair and big dark glasses. Doug owned both the Tire King and the gas station, so he tended to know what was what. Moreover, he was no gossip. But one night at dinner he mentioned what he'd seen to his wife, Lu, saying, "I don't know what to think. It being the off-season and all. And they never come up here past October." Lu just looked at him, shrugging. But she couldn't resist. She cleaned half the summer houses on the lake. She wasn't surprised, she told her various employers as she vacuumed and mopped the following June. Tommy? He was that kind of man. There were men like him everywhere: afraid of death, they were; afraid of the natural aging process; afraid to let go. And it didn't hurt that Tommy was wealthy, though where exactly his wealth came from no one knew, but then again, none of the summer people were exactly impoverished. The poorest of the lot was Eric Zamboni, and he'd had a nice little insurance business in northern New Jersey, which he'd managed to sell for a tidy profit before retiring and spending all his summers on the lake. Even then he'd remained a modest, quiet sort of man, happily puttering around the low-lying, drafty three-bedroom cottage that, at one point, had been the dining hall of a girls' camp. When he finally married his retired schoolteacher, in late August a full three years after she'd started showing up at the lake and insisting that the only way to make a real mint julep was with real mint, preferably of the home-grown variety, he did nothing in the way of home improvement other than change the name on the mailbox, and his bride—Mary—didn't seem to mind in the least.

So that was that: all of them married, all to more or less reasonably-aged and faded women, many of them widows themselves, with grown children and grandchildren and a high delight to find that, for them, there was a second act after all. All but Donald Frye, that is. It was three years, then four, then five, and Donald didn't seem the slightest bit interested in finding someone to spend his remaining years with. When you asked him how he was, he'd always look slightly distracted, as if he didn't recognize you, but then he'd snap out of it and, smiling, say, "I'm still here, aren't I?"

"Maybe he feels that there'll never be another woman he can love as much as he loved Nedra," you'd hear.

"Maybe he just isn't interested."

"Maybe he's content with his grandchildren and his dogs."

"Not everyone feels the need to remarry."

"Maybe he just hasn't met the right one."

But such explanations, offered at cookouts and birthday parties, weren't satisfying, and in any event, Donald was rarely alone. In fact, after the first quiet years of tightly-held pain, Donald's social life swung into high gear. The first few women he brought to the lake were young—far younger than he was, in their early or mid-forties, the same ages as his own three daughters. At first, they seemed carbon copies of one another, with bad divorces behind them, and an uncertain financial future, but then a pattern began to emerge, with each succeeding too-young woman becoming more stable and robust, more independent and hopeful, than the one before. Thus a struggling artist was replaced by a physical therapist, who in turn was replaced by a college professor (anthropology), who gave way to a woman who owned a stable in northwest Connecticut, who finally succumbed to an investment banker, who herself disappeared in the wake of a pediatrician. It was hard to really keep track—though God knows we tried—because sometimes the woman would only last for a single weekend, sometimes as little as a single overnight. "Got to hand it to him," people said.

"At least he's not moping around, thinking about Nedra."

"Behold what Viagra has wrought."

"May he live and be happy."

"His daughters couldn't be too thrilled."

"It's his September song."

Among the women there were questions of sex itself: How much and how often? How long did it last and how inventive was it? How important was it, at a certain age? Was it accomplished in the usual way? Or had it been replaced, by and large, by something approximating snuggling? We wanted to know, we were curious and eager, because we ourselves, the no-longer-young-ones, had been married by now for twenty, twenty-five, thirty years. We ourselves had floppy stomachs and soft upper arms and streaks of gray in our hair, and what once had been spontaneous and natural and easy no longer was, and we wondered at ourselves, and at our husbands, and children, and especially, when we were washing dishes or pulling laundry in off the line (something we all did on the lake, though God knows we wouldn't have dreamed of putting up drying lines in our backyards in the suburbs), at our neighbors. We were either the recently-arrived, with money made on Wall Street, or the long-grown children of parents who had bought the old camp cottages and tumble-down guest houses and converted them to summer houses when we were tiny, in the nineteen-fifties and sixties—it was we who had been raised on stories about how, once upon a time, the entire region was dotted with summer camps, where our parents had spent their own summers playing tennis and learning how to canoe, only now…who can afford it? And even if you could, there were all those other, competing activities for youngsters, summers in Europe or trekking through the Andes, and the days of eating s'mores around the campfire and Color War were over. But the place—the place itself, with its wonderful clean aromas…pine, Queen Ann's lace, rain…and miraculously clear water—remained. "Aren't we the lucky ones?" our parents would tell us. And we were.

Then the women Donald invited up became even younger—thirtyish and never-before-married, or thirty-six, with a baby in tow. And there were young men, too, graduate-student types, struggling playwrights, wistful save-the-worlders, spending weeks at a time at the Fryes' boxy house on a spit of land that divided the long western half of the lake from the shorter, wider eastern part. Were the women friends of his daughters? It seemed unlikely. Were the men gay? What was Donald up to as he rounded the corner into his eighties, his hair as silver and thick as ever, his eyes as blue? Unlike most of the other widowers on the lake, he'd never retired, but rather taken sabbaticals to care for his ailing wife. Now his name, and the name of his company, began to appear in the pages of the Boston papers. It was a small investment bank, people said. Or not. It was a holding company. It was a brokerage house. It was none of these things, instead an export-import business, something to do with orange juice pulp. Donald flew to Argentina. He flew to China. He flew to Vietnam. He had gotten into the cell phone business. He was expanding computer services in the former Eastern bloc. But when you asked him—and we did—he demurred. "Business is boring," he'd say. "Let's talk about something else. Reading anything good?"

There was no more to do at the Fryes' house than at anyone else's (unless of course you counted the sprawling—some said ostentatious—Trowbridge place, with its tennis court and speedboat), but perhaps, like Nedra, the young men and women who came to visit amused themselves by taking long soulful walks, or by collecting pinecones and wild daisies, or by reading. The Frye house had a real library, everything from Sherlock Holmes to Beowulf to the latest Stephen King. Once, years earlier, when she was still feeling well enough to take jaunts into town, Nedra had come back from the annual library sale with the complete works of Shakespeare, bound in faded red, with commentary by some Oxford don. Perhaps they were in there reading *A Midsummer Night's Dream*. The one thing that was certain was that one of them got out Nedra's box of paints and re-painted the mailbox, covering it with twisting vines and butterflies, all deep greens and soft purplish blue.

Nedra had been a beautiful woman—even in her last illness, she was beautiful, with incredible high cheekbones and a wide mouth and dimples—but the thirtyish friends (companions? lovers?) of Donald were, on the whole, unremarkable. On the other hand, they were young: there were women in scant bathing suits, appearing in public in mini-skirts and tight pants. The men often went around in nothing more than a pair of shorts, their feet thrust into sandals. Sometimes they accompanied Donald on the long walks he took with his dogs. Donald's own daughters, in the meantime, came around less and less often. I'd grown up with them—summer after summer on the lake. I missed seeing them, hearing about their adult lives and watching their children grow up. But Donald didn't seem to mind.

The people who minded were the other husbands—not the widowers, who, as a group, seemed wonderfully content with their second wives (even the smarmy Tommy Tompkins appeared at social gatherings visibly delighted by his second wife, Ray, who'd long since let her white-blonde hair go white-gray, and told stories about her grandchildren's exploits.) Rather, it was the younger set, the now-middle-aged children of the first homeowners, their sons and sons-in-law, who looked at us, at their wives of many years, and saw heartbreak. They turned towards us and saw what they'd always seen—contentment and comfort and understanding, trust and love and a long history of working-things-out—and then they looked towards Donald Frye's boxy house set back from the rocks by a strip of grass and blueberry bushes and ungrown evergreen underbrush, and they knew that there was—there had to be—more.

Betsy Yates' husband actually had an affair, but it was stupid—he took up with an extravagantly dressed local woman who suffered from anxiety attacks and had two ex-husbands—and it petered out almost before it began, with the usual trips to the marriage counselor and the gym to patch things over. Joanna Anthony's husband became terribly depressed, and ended up losing thirty pounds before finally declaring that he was sick and tired of being a lawyer, and really just wanted to teach piano, which meant that Joanna herself had to go back to work as a landscape architect, which wasn't something she really wanted to do again, at least not full time. Lil Hutchinson's husband sold his orthodontic practice and went back to school to study comparative religion. One of Donald Frye's own sons-in-law, the British diplomat who'd married my friend Beth (and weren't the rest of us girls on the lake envious of Beth for her debonair husband with his clipped BBC speech and elegant bearing?), announced that he had fallen in love with a staff lawyer at the Justice Department, packed his bags, and left his wife, stunned and startled and utterly undone, in their modern house in the Virginia suburbs.

As for me: slowly at first and then not so slowly, Charlie lost interest. When I asked him what was going on, when I prodded him for his thoughts, for his moods, when I suggested that we were going through changes together, and that change was the essence and very timbre of life, he'd just gaze at the floor, or at his feet resting on the floor, or sometimes at the carpet. Our own children (boy-girl twins) were halfway through college; our own dog, Larry, was creeping around on arthritic legs; our marriage had had its ups and downs. And yet—and yet! We laughed at the same jokes, enjoyed the same movies, bought tribal rugs and used crockery together. And, too, there was sex—not as often, or as passionate, as it had been, once—before children—before illness—before worries—before, before. I looked to the mirror and knew I saw what my own mother, and her mother before her, saw: a woman whose beauty and intense charm were gone.

* * *

Six summers after Nedra Frye died, her husband holding her hand, Donald Frye's house remained shuttered. It wasn't just that he no longer filled its rooms with men and women in the full flush and strength of not-yet-middle-aged adulthood, but, somewhat shockingly, he and his dogs didn't come as well. They didn't come in June, they didn't come in July, and by the time August rolled around, people were saying that he'd put the house on the market, and it was all very hush-hush, as he didn't want anyone—even his daughters—to know that he was unloading it. Where *were* the daughters, for that matter? Our summers had been entangled well into college, when all four of us finally spun out and away—me to graduate school (in art history) and then to London (for my post-doc) and finally back home, to a job at a small college in Connecticut and a husband who said, on our first date, that he wanted at least three children, and the Frye girls to their own futures, in Los Angeles and Nashville and Washington, D.C.

"Three children?" I'd said, terrified, as I gazed into my future husband's lean, intelligent face.

"Or four. Five. Two. As long as we have them."

One night, after our twins (busy with their own lives) had come and gone, my husband turned to me in bed and said: "Put down your book." I was re-reading *The Brothers Karamazov*, amazed by how much of it I'd forgotten. Taking the book from me, he rolled over onto his side. I thought he was going to embrace me in a prelude to love-making. He was wearing striped pajamas with a button missing where his ribs met his belly in an inverted V. I was wearing an old, oversized t-shirt. The house we were in had once been the gatekeeper's house at a summer lodge. My parents had bought it in 1950, just before I was born, adding a modern kitchen which was no longer modern, a bathroom, and an outdoor shower. They'd stopped coming up the same year that Mother had gone into assisted living, in Baltimore, though when I talked to her—to them—on the phone, begging them to make the trip, telling them that I would fetch them myself, that I'd rent a big comfortable car for the journey—they always promised they would think about it. There was rain rolling in from the west. You could hear it coming in from New Hampshire, how it held to the tops of the mountains. I was suddenly gripped by a great and terrible desire to go to Paris and see the Picassos there, a desire like a seizure, like a shower of electricity in my brain.

"Jules," he said—his pet name for me, of course, as professionally I am always "Julia": Dr. Julia Sanders. "Jules" itself was just a precursor for the more playful pet names: "Jewels," "Rubies," "Pearl."

"Charlie," I answered back. He stretched, arching his back so his chest nestled closer to my shoulder.

Could I? Would I? After the seasons of indifference, I wasn't sure I could summon the old desire, though perhaps, I thought, I could whip something up—engaging in some spurious dirty fantasies, some of the more salacious movies and TV shows I'd recently seen.

"It's just," he said, "that I don't quite know what to do anymore. Not professionally so much. I like my work—my career is in good shape." Charlie was a contractor, with his own design-and-build firm. His clients tended to want the natural look, restoring their crumbling 19$^{th}$-century multi-family homes to their original gambrel-roofed majesty, with new wraparound porches, or slate and copper roofing. Our interests—mine in art, his in design—dovetailed. We'd always understood each other. That was the beauty of it.

"What do you mean?" I said.

"It's not the kids either, though, I don't know. I miss having them around. I don't feel old enough to have kids who don't need me anymore."

"They still need you."

"To pay their tuition," he said. "And it's not you, either. It's me. I know it's me but I don't know what it is about me that's the problem. It's almost, I don't know."

"What?"

"Do you ever think that we—you and I—didn't so much make a profound mistake, as that we're still pretending, still acting, almost, as if we were in a play, as if we knew what we're doing but really are merely hurtling along, *faking it,* putting on the face of husband and wife, of father and mother, of professionals—the mortgage, the kids in college, your vegetable garden, all of it—when really it's just sort of, I don't know, *thin.* Like we're merely skating on the surface of life, thinking that the ice *is* life, but really, the real stuff, the real life, is the pond beneath, all that dark water."

"Where it's cold. Where, if you fell in, you'd probably drown."

"Or maybe not. Maybe you'd just be shocked by the cold. Maybe you'd just know something you didn't know before."

"Or maybe you'd die."

"Maybe," he said. Then he said: "Do you remember that girl I dated in college, Jessica?"

"What about her?"

"I read in the alum magazine that she'd adopted a child from China."

"Isn't she kind of old to become a mommy?"

"I guess not."

"Okay," I said, sitting up a little in the dim dark light. "So she adopted a child from China. This leads you to conclude what exactly?"

"I don't know," my husband said. "It just got me thinking, is all."

Of course I remembered Jessica—not that I'd ever met her. She'd been mean to my husband during their college romance, and he'd been obsessed with her. She ended up marrying and divorcing a real estate developer in Atlantic City, and then remarrying, this time to an older man with a huge income from the investments that his own father, a sharp and hungry Irishman, had made just before the Second World War. I knew all this because, on occasion, Charlie would tell me stories. He told those same stories to the twins, too, but without the detail. For me it was: "She was wearing this garish black t-shirt with, I don't know, holes in it or something, very upscale, and these pink cowboy boots, and on a dare she was standing on a table in the college pub, singing, even though she couldn't sing worth a lick, and she actually put her foot up, put it on my forehead, and you know, I was basically her slave..." Whereas to them it was: "She was flat-out nuts. She wore these outrageous costumes, and at parties, Jesus, she could really go over the top."

Whenever he told me about her, he always finished up the same way, by saying that, had it not been for me, he didn't know what might have become of him. "You're my center," he'd say, "the warm sun around which I revolve. Around which we *all* revolve. Without you, there'd be no me." I always smiled when he told me such things, and, believing them myself, took them as my due. But now, as he gazed blankly at the ceiling—he'd returned to lying on his back—what had once been merely a whisper, a subtext of a subtext, became glaringly obvious, a shrieking, electronic billboard. Who wants to spend a lifetime in predictable, orderly orbit?

I thought then about asking him what Jessica's Chinese baby had to do with us, or, more precisely, with him, but I didn't know how to put the question in a way that would solicit any other answer than one that would break me clear in two.

He answered my unspoken question anyway, saying: "Don't you ever wonder to yourself what your life might have been if you and I had never met?"

* * *

Donald Frye came back at the end of the summer, this time with an older woman in tow, whom he introduced as his friend. Her name was Elsa, she had an indeterminate accent, and one glance told you that she'd never been pretty. She had thinning yellowish hair; a sharp nose; a chin that met at a soft point; and a vulnerable-looking neck. Her body was square and thick; her legs were mottled with varicose veins; her feet were wide. Her eyes, however, were bright, green around the edges and blue at their centers. She wore sunhats and clogs and big, billowing dresses, and said that she'd never wanted to be married, and wasn't going to start now. No one took to her—not really, anyway—but she and Donald were seen, at least twice a day, walking Donald's dogs and calling them by all kinds of endearments: "Honey Buckets of Love," "Whisker Snap," "Paws," "Boo Boo of My Heart." He was as handsome as ever, if older, stooping slightly now around the shoulders, and growing his hair longer in front, to mask a bald patch.

One afternoon when I'd managed to cajole Charlie into joining me to pick the blueberries that grew wild and scrubby near the edge of the lake at a place that everyone, for unknown reasons, called "the sliver," we heard the sounds of raised voices, and turned to see Elsa striding furiously forward, her chest puffed out and puffing, her bare, yellowing, mottled legs scraping against the underbrush. Coming up behind her was Donald, saying: "Come on, sweetest, you know I didn't mean it that way." When she saw Charlie and me stooping, pails in hand, over the blueberry bushes, Elsa stopped. A moment later, Donald came up behind her: he was wearing faded red shorts, sandals, and an old button-down shirt, frayed at the collar and cuffs, its sleeves pulled up to just below his elbows. He put his hands on Elsa's shoulders. "Blueberry pie or blueberry pancakes?" he said.

"How are you?" Charlie said.

"Both," I said.

"You know Elsa, of course," Donald said, still standing just behind her, his hands still resting on her shoulders. "And Elsa, you remember Julie—Julie and Charlie? Julie and my girls grew up together, I guess you could say."

"Hello again," Elsa said.

"What do you hear from the kids?" he continued, indicating our own children, each of whom had come up to the lake for one last, brief weekend before returning to their real lives, and I was about to say something neutral about their studies—or maybe it was about how much I missed them?—but before either Charlie or I had the chance to say anything, Donald went on: "Hard to believe it, really. Little Julie Berg, all grown up, and married, and with nearly grown-up children of her own. Hot damn. You and Beth used to read comic books under the covers together. And sneak off at night, when you thought we were asleep. You didn't know that we knew, but we did. We figured you girls couldn't get into much harm, not up here. And now, look at you, a bonafide adult. How did that happen?"

"I don't know," I said.

"I know," Elsa said.

"Elsa knows everything," Donald said, and with that, he flashed one of his broadest, whitest smiles, squeezed Elsa's shoulders, whispered something into her ear, and turned back in the direction he had come from, Elsa following one pace behind.

"What was *that?"* Charlie said when they were out of earshot.

"What do you mean?"

"'Blueberry pie or blueberry pancakes?' Was he always so smug?"

"I don't know. I thought he was fine."

"He looks like the cat who swallowed the canary. And what's with his new friend? Now he's into Nazis?"

"I think she's Dutch."

"You don't know any more than I do. You're just making that up."

We had only just started collecting the blueberries, such that between us we barely had two fistfuls, but now Charlie started ripping out whole branches, plunking them into his pail, leaves and all. "I don't know, Jules," he said. "And maybe I'm just being a jerk, but the man has always struck me as being such a narcissistic, condescending creep. 'Little Julie, all grown up.' What does he expect? He himself is so old he's nearly dead. Oh, I know: he was such a great husband, he didn't ask to be a widower, he's doing the best he can, he has such wonderful eyes, such energy." With that, he stopped denuding the blueberry bushes, and sat down on a rock.

"What are you really saying, Charlie?" I finally asked. "You're getting old? I am? Or is it that Donald is too old to get away with the kinds of things that you stopped doing in your twenties?"

"Now you're being silly. Did you even hear a word of what I just said? I merely said—"

"That you think he's a narcissistic, condescending creep. So what? No one said you had to like him."

"You like him, though. He's part of your magical, perfect childhood."

"What?"

"You idealize him, in fact."

"Why are we arguing about Donald Frye?"

"I'm not arguing," Charlie said.

"Look on the bright side," I said after a little while, talking mainly because I felt I had to say something, to have proof that the world had retained its customary shape and texture. "He stopped chasing teenagers. Maybe he'll even settle down and marry this woman. At least she seems to give him a run for his money."

"Exactly," Charlie said, as overhead, a cormorant soared into the sky, and inside my body, my bones went cold.

* * *

Donald and Elsa never did marry—though for years there was talk of another wedding on the lake, another wedding to follow the weddings of first my daughter and then, finally, her twin brother, and of Stu Levine's second wife's middle-aged Buddhist daughter, and the various American grandchildren of the French wife of Tommy Tompkins, and Donald's own divorced daughter, Beth—the one I'd known best, the one I'd loved most. On the other hand—well, there was no other hand. Donald's Elsa stayed on, and gradually people began to like her well enough, or at least to forget that there'd been a time when they hadn't liked her at all, a time when they'd asked, openly, what the handsome and dashing Donald Frye could see in such a woman.

One day shortly after the birth of our own first grandchild—a girl—Charlie turned to me and said: "You know, not once did I ever think of having an affair."

"I'm glad."

"Did you?"

"Did I what?"

"Ever think of having an affair?"

"Of course not," I said.

"I mean," he said. "I could have. I guess. Had I wanted to. But it always seemed, I don't know, like such a waste of time."

"I know," I said, though I was only saying words. By now, Donald Frye was stretching into real old age, first with a cane, and now with a walker, usually with a hired helper by his side—an endless stream of kindly black women with various accents denoting the islands. Elsa herself barely came at all: we heard she wasn't well. Others at the lake were aging too; tiptoeing into what we all hoped would be a gentle, unimaginative death. They were true, all those clichés about life's brevity. Meanwhile, Charlie and I lived quietly, usually at peace, like two ponies in side-by-side stalls.

I looked at my husband of thirty-odd years, at his dark brown eyes, at his characteristic expression of slightly disdainful bewilderment, at his thinning sand-colored hair, and knew that he was just as big a liar as I—with my remorseless optimism, my willed cheerfulness, my love of the ordinary and desperation for safety. Even so, I was glad that, if he *had* had an affair, he never told me about it. I was glad that he was as skilled at deception as I was.

"Such a waste," he repeated.

"I know just what you mean," I said again, but I didn't, not really. Not when I thought about all those summers spent on the lake, me and the Frye girls, Karin, Nina, Beth, the four of us sneaking off in the moonlight, via canoe, heading for the sliver, where we'd meet boys—all those boys, and where had they come from, and where had they gone? —and where we'd let our bikinis slide off as easily as if they were wrapping paper. As we lay on our backs in the scrappy, sandy earth, the smell of blueberries filled our nostrils and our bodies became strange and terrifying and beautiful and obscene, and every now and then, one of us would fall irreparably in love.

## *Trying Not to Forget*

On the last day in my mother's country,
my grandfather says I could speak Dayak
fluently if I could just stay one more month,
a little plea in English that would keep
the only grandchild who left the island
from leaving again, but the weak tether
of language is already unraveling.
At that moment I think I could learn
to walk barefoot on concrete in the mornings,
step from the house he built of jackwood
and cement, out to the square he carved
from jungle to grow long beans—that hang
as if on a clothesline—and gather them
for a meal. I would take home drinks
in plastic bags stuck with a straw
and encircled by a rubber band. I'll stop
misstepping at the deep gutters along
every road, which remind me of the lines
in his palms that have learned to channel silt
and rain and blood away to wherever
they are determined to go. He folds
the useless hope into a leaf with a betelnut
anointed with white powder from a rusting tin.
It goes back into his mouth, but he does not
swallow; he lets the wish sit with his teeth
staining red, or *bireh*—one of the words
I'm trying not to forget.

# *Request for a War Story*

*for Babai*

My father's strabismus wandered
away from Vietnam, another
pair in a line of failing eyes
that kept our family out of war.

But my mother's father tells me
he remembers Japanese planes over Borneo,
perforating the top of the forest like
hornbills descending with calls for ghosts

to leave this earth. He harbored
a British soldier in the house
he built on stilts. He says this
without regret or pride, just recalls

how it felt to kneel against his own porch,
the way soldiers forced his lip to the plastic
rim of a bucket, the mouthfuls
of salt water to save someone else's life.

## Jacqueline Kudler

# *After the Long Bitter Season*

Each day in April, they are here again,
high on the open slopes, under the pine,
beside the suddenly garrulous streams,
pushing up from last summer's cemeteries:
the iris, the lupine, the baby blue eyes.
and we are waiting for each new appearance—
each new signal of redemption—
the earth returning to us again
after the long bitter season.

I want to talk about the Calypso orchids,
here this Wednesday all at once—
two days of the sun's touch just enough
to coax them out from the cold.
Winged pink petals on leafless stems,
they grow where least expected,
the ground rocky, inhospitable, shrouded
with sparse dead pine shards.

Each year we think to find them
in a kinder context, the new, tender
grasses of a meadow, perhaps, but no,
this is the soil, the shade, the hardship
that sustains them.
I want to sit down on this stony hilltop,
in the middle of this bitter year,
watch how the orchids
launch their pink parachutes out
between one darkness
and another.

## *Desert Ecology 38: Umbrelliferae*

Here's the secret to thriving
in this desert: taking part in Ammi
majus' existence— glabrous herb

sprouting in cultivated land. Listen
intently till you hear the lower leaves of each
Bishop's weed withering at anthesis.

Though you be heavy, notice
how each fruiting umbrel opens
as if in flight. And though darkness

appears to reign, how each one—
long-peduncled—reflects one ray
of mysterious, glorious light.

# *Desert Ecology 52: Gramineae*

Entering the desert without disturbing
one narrow leaf-blade of Cutandia
or Cynodon (star grass), questions of
science give way to humble reasoning
and sky meditation—imagining no
pipelines, no oil flares to soil the air,
nothing but aromatic grasses like
lemony Cymbopogon parkeri, vast
infinity, Dichanthium and Digitaria
bringing me back to sky mind, desert
mind, each inflorescence a sketch of
fleeting nature, life's essence.

The silence of Eleusine compressa
entering the heart, its wiry stolen-like stems
creeping along sandy depressions.
Eragrostis, love grass—its spikelets
gracefully dancing in the shade of
Ziziphus and acacia bushes.
Vitally present, infinite grasses,
I drink a toast to them: sturdy and lucid,
braced against the shamal, fluid in
alluvial and fine deposits, on sand hills,
in damp fields, in waste moist places
of the rodat, in ditches, channels, sandy
depressions.

Staring into the sun without blinking,
each tuft and pedicel, culm and panicle
a dreamsong rising up into the bluest
sky. Look how the lemon-yellow bees
and desert whites come at their beck
and call, how they lift you high above
the parched, cracked earth to float
on the notes of the desert lark.
The Cistanche having all burned
to a brown crisp, pray you'll have praise
enough till your dying day for the persistent
grasses and the breeze that sets them
to nodding in agreement with life.

# *Gardener's Dream in the Desert*

> Remember, it is forbidden to live in a town which has no garden or greenery.
>
> —*Kiddushin 4:12*

After China, I returned bent
on building a humble hermitage
beside a lily pond or stream
surrounded by bamboo. After
Sausalito, a houseboat seemed the
only way to go—and lining my dock
with California poppies. After
walking the Camino de Santiago,
lavender was all I wanted to grow.
Reading Tolstoy, I vowed to trade my
paved-over cosmopolitan world
for a rural estate and live like a peasant
among fields of sunflowers.

But we all know how these things
go—wanting one thing and
ending up with its opposite.
Living in the desert now, laboring
over my tiny patio garden, I
imagine bamboo, poppies,
lavender, sunflowers growing
luxuriantly beyond my hermitage
houseboat on my rural estate at
the opposite end of this world.

But resisting cursing desert sun
and saline soil, I marvel how the desert flora
humble me to see with clarity all that lies
between Fish and Moon.

In the desert noon, only one desire:
to fall eventually like rain to earth
and turn to herb, or into the sea and

emerge as pearl. Each dusk I pluck
yellow leaves from budless shrubs that all
day long have shrugged their spindly branches
at the sun, and I ask that I might be kept
"one day full fed and one day hungry,"*
and that the desert hyacinths (dhanoun) —
those radiant root parasites, might bloom,
however briefly, this year.

Leslie Ringold, photograph

*from the *Kashf al-Mahjub*, oldest Persian treatise on Sufism, by al-Hujwar

# *Upside Down World Under the Last Peony*

The vase—a clear glass globe,
tear-shaped, but recognizable as our world,

holds a peony, cut down yesterday before the rain,
the bud tight as a baby's angry fist, but now

opening slowly into this new day,
each translucent petal pulling in the light.

The stem of the flower slants, as if mirroring
earth's invisible axis, the blossom at true north,

where, as I write, polar bears, disoriented
and starving, prowl their diminishing ice.

Inside the globe, the tree line outside my window
has been captured, but upended—the clear blue sky,

one white cloud floating, east to west, pushed down
into the bottom of the globe. You away—

your watch set eight hours later (almost upside down)
and our great white dog—only one week dead.

## Thomas Patterson

# *Summering at the Rossers, Roaring Spring, 1953*

The year we learned what being brother and sister meant
they dropped us off at the Rossers
we walked toward the door lowering our heads, believing
we had done something wrong—
the gate rail bent backward, a fearsome gothic thing

the trees were filled with summer birds
the sparrow weaker than the crow

the creek had as its future the long funnel
washing into the dry bed mouth—

you kept a picture of our mother in your pocket
called "sisters, 1942"—she's wading in the river
pale arms around Aunt Veda's shoulders
the dusk building behind them seemed a great hawk's quilted wings—

the smoke from two cigarettes blossomed in our lungs
down in the fort we built beneath
the coal bin in just one week's time—

you took hold of my hand and we left that place
running from darkness into darkness
delivered from the people who pretended to care—

ahead, the Juniata River ran toward
the gilded valley of the Susquehanna, carrying its stories
of girls-in-waiting and their ruined dreams
of boys coming home from Le Teil, Ploesti and the Saar
numbed into silence—

its own tiny arc of love and loss—

its histories were our own.

# *Ravensbrük Dissociative, 1943*

The garden roses loved you and they trembled
as though your fingers brushed against
each crimson throat,

smooth clouds warned carefully, *verboten*
wondering if you would ever come back
and why you left with Nessa when she said it was time to go

down through the tunnel under the house
out into the mirrored darkness, broken in two
by searing stars;

right away the Kapo asked you to agree, *ja*
that your yellow hair meant nothing, *ja*
that your blue eyes were a lie;

it all began the day you stepped down *auf der strasse*
practicing a cabriole learned at the academy—
the street was sunlit then—yet how could that be—

weren't you already there when the guard led Nessa
toward the group of newly inspected women
and then pointed to you,

*kommen hier zu mir*—
ending with a glib
*das is das*—

after that you heard nothing
saw nothing
wanted nothing again;

every moment it feels that you will stumble
falling down into the funnel of damp air
a lonely child again in Abba's garden

looking up through the cylinder of darkness
into the lip of the stars that might save you
dreaming their shapes into distances.

## Jodi L. Hottel

# *Letter to Nisei Soldier, 1944*

*—after a linocut by Henry Sugimoto*

The baby squirms in my arms. But I am far away—with you.

So much I want—for you to return from Italy, to meet Sumio, your son. For this constant, gritty wind to cease, the suffocating heat to stop. To look out the window and not see a guard tower glaring at me. To have our two-month-old son grow up free, as an American should.

The face of a sunflower has climbed to our window. Yes, from the seeds you planted before shipping out. I tend it as though it has the power to keep you alive. Its face greets me each morning, like Sumi's. He looks just like you. Two faces, full of life.

Night in Amache
beyond guard towers, barbed wire—
flickering desert sky.

# *Plum Branches*

I snip tender limbs
knobbed with tight purple swells,
stand their legs in warm water
and wait—
impossibly delicate
pink petals
force darkness open
and sing.

From the collection of the Editor, photograph

# *White Rabbit*

The Summer of Love was over,
everywhere. It was now December
in New York, the weather and the war
bitter and getting worse. Who could
have guessed this was the calm before
the calamity, hurricanes of blood
just months away. I was only fifteen,
no LSD in my loose-leaf binder but
on the same bad trip with the rest
of America. Maybe it was a Tuesday
when I stepped off the school bus into
the four o'clock dark. Bracing myself for
the quarter-mile walk against the wind,
a flash of white caught my eye under
the corner mailbox. I walked closer,
thinking what, I don't know, maybe
someone's cat or yesterday's snow.
I bent down to look and there it was—
not snow but a snow-white rabbit.
Not Alice's or the Airplane's, this one
real and nearly frozen. I picked it up
feeling its heart race against my hand,
its two pink eyes no doubt wondering
if things had gone from bad to worse.
Do I have to tell you the odds of finding
a white rabbit, frozen or not, on a
New York City street? Or the odds of
me at fifteen, all hormones and cliché,
giving a rat's ass either way? Jimi
was asking, *Are you experienced?*
Cassius Clay was Muhammad Ali.
The Summer of Love was over,
never having made it to Detroit,
Newark, the Sinai or Dak To.
And what had I done besides clench
my fist, cop a few feels and curse LBJ?
I was only fifteen, pathetic and small,

white and privileged as a princess phone.
The world was going to hell on roller skates.
I tucked the rabbit inside my coat
and headed home.

James Andrew Smith, *Inspiriting Habliments of Indigo and Brown,*
oil on panel, 20" x 20"

# *Pear Tree*

The scale had finally tipped. The crown
had leaned the trunk's coarse twist
too far, had torn the root
from the earth's socket.
Rain moistened the dry rot
into marrow, a paste of henna
coating the frayed tongue. Yet the bud-pearls
went on loosening, day by day whitening
the twig wood. Perhaps
it could still drink the rain.
Perhaps sap rises and rises its fill
like a tide, urged by the novae of transient stars.
Winter rye grew tall between the branches.
Each day I chewed
one rasping blade, folding it greedily
into my mouth. The sweet blood foaming,
stinging my throat.
Today I stood before a tissue of sunlight, behind which
the gilt cage burned. Sparks
lifted off it, and drifted fading down.
I stepped inside,
and the wail of bees rose around me.
I stood; they knocked against me, settling
their squirming burrs on my hair.
I have no flowers for you, I said
and crossed through that veil.

## *Trees were responsible for the seasons*

Charlie came to this conclusion at seven when
Ms. Wu, about to release them for
recess, looked out the window and announced:

Look! Spring is here! As if someone
she had been expecting had just got off the bus.
The children rushed to press their faces

on the glass, and there Spring
was: a tulip waking up from its flower-
bed, petals paused in the shape of a yawn.

Charlie thought about this on
the way home, and using the fantastic cause-and-effect
logic of children, decided that tulips brought

Spring. Seasons come from growing. And it made
sense—Mr. Johnson at the end of the street sold Christmas
trees, and that always seemed to happen just before

Winter. In fact, Charlie decided that
the number of Christmas trees must correlate (though
he didn't use this word) with the amount of snow

that falls down. And in Autumn, it's the
red leaves budding. Someone once told him that
green leaves turn orange then red in

Autumn, but now he's not so sure: the
red leaves must grow out—that's how they bring in
the season. But what about the green ones

that were there first? They
must get sucked back into the wood, like
snails when you poke them, to make space for the

red ones. When the reds fall, the
greens grow back out again, eventually, when
they hear Tulip is back. But what about Summer? Jack had

asked him the day after, probing the soft center of this
wonderful new knowledge with eager fingers. A tricky
question, but Charlie explained that

he was a kind of tree, and so was Jack: children
always grow the most in June and July—children are
Summer's Trees. And how

perfect, it seemed to him,
the way the world works—in youth's
days of growing, so did the Summer Dog Days seem

far from longing.

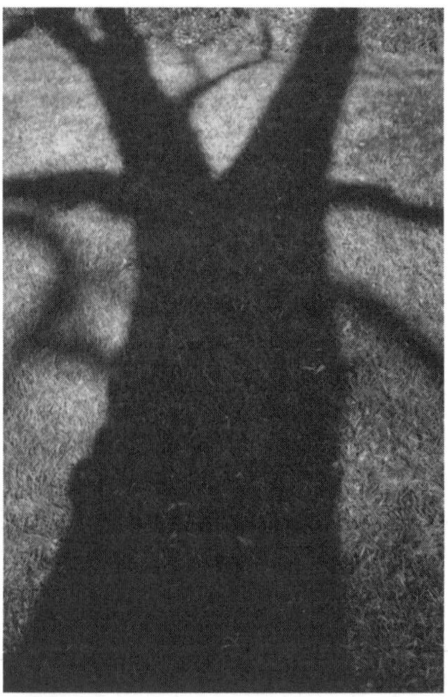

From the collection of the Editor, photograph

# *Reformasi*

A revolution, they say, on
the Malay peninsula.

But, here, there is
no party. No
confetti. No victim,
rapist, criminal. No
conspiracy, lie,
set-up. No tyranny. No
betrayal. No poverty. No
justice. No starvation, no
child. Only

my grandmother making
tea in the morning—no milk,
a little sugar, the way she likes—
listening to the sound of
industry in the
peaceful praying morning
of the kampung. How much it is
like a cloud of light, like good

disease. There are dew-drops dangling
on the tips of the bowing fingers of
grass; the quiet tapioca is
in its bed of soil, for tomorrow, in
milky drips. The
paddy fields are thriving on
the flood, drowsy in the soft
muddy mattress. The taste of rice
is sleepy, as the steamy mist-filled

hills must dream. We count
the fish grandfather brings
home—ten, twenty. There is no
poison in them, no snake, no
fertilizer. No march, no

picket, no injustice. No
new law. No necessity. No
scraping pen, no
newspaper cutting. No mother,
no child. No party. No
confetti. Only the

crumpled paper ball of
a Malayan morning
unfolding

from blood-spilled grounds.

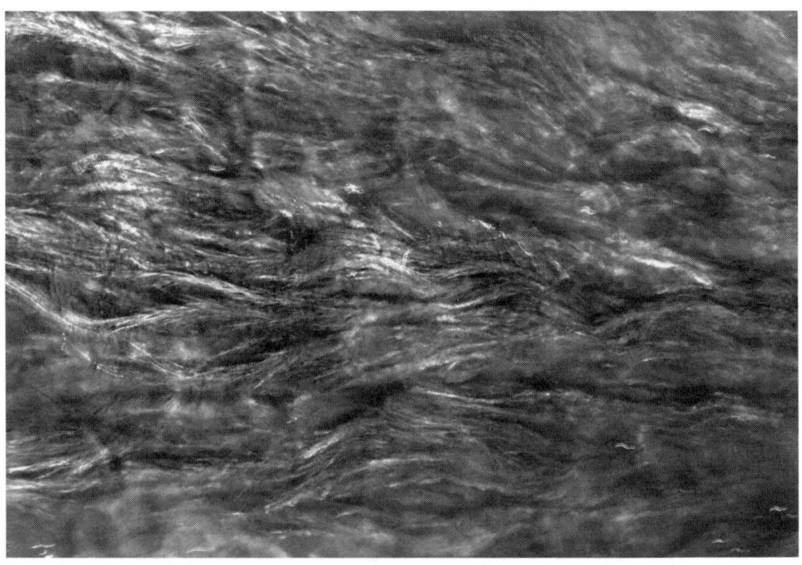

Roi J. Tamkin, *Water Abstract,* photograph

## *In My Father's Absence*

Men make women messy,
my mother loved to vent
while supervising pickups
of plastic soldiers from my room.
But I was six, too young
to count the dead,
too full of spunk to quake
before the high-pitched chorus
echoing each *a capella* rant.
Perhaps the better half of God
once raised her voice
while ordering untidy worlds,
rewinding wind and whirlpools,
boxing ears and grounding boats.
I see her on the seventh evening
watching leaves and snow
descend in whorls like cereal and sugar
her ragamuffin children stir and spill
among the twigs and burls,
the wooden blocks and battle gear
she reads like bones,
then sweeps from forest floors.

# *Grandfather's Funeral, Orthodox Sephardic Synagogue, Los Angeles*

We are separated in the foyer.
Father and my younger brother
invited into the great hall with the other men,
while grandmother and I are barred entry.
Instead, we are ushered up interior stairs
to a gallery where women
and some other teen-age girls
are concealed
behind a wooden screen.

We may not pray aloud nor sing.
We peer through leaf-pattern scroll-work,
our faces and bodies properly forgotten,
as men raise their voices in praise of my grandfather
who would drop a dollop of butter
into my soft-boiled eggs,
recite poems he'd written
and ask me questions each week
about how I was doing
in school.

The balcony is stuffy. It is hard to breathe.
The songs and prayers drone in my ears. Hebrew
by others for others.
Grandfather never told me that a woman's role
was to be invisible,
our life's work, silence.

I long to fly down to the temple floor,
a raven with sharpened beak,
patrol back and forth
across the top of his coffin,
flinty eyes toward heaven,
railing against
the thief.

## *The Ambiguity of Stone*

I want to believe the last time
I saw him no language was needed
between us, a dive lure flaring
like a tiny orange flame between rubber
night crawlers as a breath from
my mouth entered his. Frost
had taken the ground the week
before. Everything seemed ready
to harden or split wide, tractor parts
lodged in stiff dirt, the mulberry's
sap clogged by cold. Even now,
I want to believe eternity exists
in that corner of the lake where we once
saw Bobby Gary take a BB in the eye,
where cattails forked in summer,
and on our last afternoon Nick leaned
to bait his hook. A week later,
he'd be dead. In the woods
I'd find a bike so honeycombed
with hornet nests I could taste
their wings in my chest. The whole sky
would quiver, power lines cross–
hatching clouds as if someone had
stitched them with a lightning hum.
But that last day, everything
went quiet. Pounding out dents
in the shanty, we talked of smallmouth jigs
and where the bluegills might bed
in the spring. We cast our lines,
gutting a trout that spilled its clutch
of eggs, until the last sun sank
over us the way it sinks over
quarrystone ready to be made
into church steps or garden statuary,
so that even as we packed up our things,
something inside him was waiting
to emerge as a flock of starlings

made a shadow of his face, the cold
night swallowing oldrow boats
on a shoreline it had already erased.

Darren Dirksen, *Orion's Belt,* oil on panel, 38" x 28"

# *Transposition*

*To F.*

It was like the accommodation to the sloping floor
You lamented to begin with but came to kind of adore:
The notion of making do, being able to, Girl Scoutian; the minor triumph
Of you; your liberation, the body being the beginning, the shifting things
Around: that Life is Biology for which no remedy
Exists: the turns & twistings of the flesh that used to be
Your secret joy, into the finishings: the questions of focusing
On the biases, fat with brimming & very calm.
Dying we always are. But dead.
What does that mean?

## Mary Kay Rummel

# *Vegetable Soul*

Your soul is a chosen landscape
—*Paul Verlaine*

Or maybe the soul is a still life
like Cezanne's onions—crinkled skin,
astringent flesh, pungent breath
cushioned on a table like eggs in a nest.

They add depth to a stew without
becoming the thing like the blue wash
that's part of the undercoat
part of the shadow.

His onions dance, green fingers
all grab and clabber language,
green flames sing in the hearth
in the throat of the wine bottle
the molecules that make up my skin
the air between our lips.

Or maybe the soul is the inside
of a butternut squash that I split
with a crack of the blade,
scoop seeds, oil flesh for the fire,
in my hands, generations of hands
repeating these gestures
and the anxious pleasures of testing
for doneness, the first bite that singes
the tongue and the voluptuous swallow.

Pallid offsprings of sun
warm winter bellies and glorify the bones.
Edible bodies with their miracle
of turning inside out.

# *Carrying On*

Look at how this day stains the next
how a leak in the roof will rot
a beam in the attic, how water
runs a brown-bordered river down
the wall. How the smell permeates,
how we long to hang a sheet
or move a shelf, how we search for words
to cover it all, the accident of yesterday
speaking through today. This morning
I awoke, and half the bitter twilight
hung coat-like in my closet. *Come here,*
said the dark, and wrapped me
in its long, barbed sleeves.

# *Weeping Willow*

The willow missed
the children, their chatter—
like squirrels, but more various
and musical—missed
the sparrow-light bodies pressed
against her, the secrets
they whispered, how they clung
to her branches with their small
hands, the way their legs twined
around her.

Nothing inhabited her
like that, nothing loved
so fiercely or so foolishly.
They believed they would be
hers forever,
did not understand,
at all, necessity, compulsion,

letting go

# *Sing the Long War*

I was led (I will swear I was led)
through a slit in a curtain of air,
one step farther up the sidewalk
in the shadow of a single sycamore,

into the next world (I will swear),
where everyone I loved was dead
and gauzed with dread, though all day,
the next and after, we talked and bled

as before. And look, here we are—
again tonight the sunset's red
and silver sing the long war, clearer
than the evening paper. We dead

still stand, openmouthed, hands
in the air, nails unable to shred
the invisible cloth (we will swear)—
it's thin as shadow but will not tear.

## Cory Brown

# *Not Yet*

It's that dreamlike season again between
summer and fall, not yet fall, the old grumpy
busdriver who tells you to sit down he'll
get you to where you're going don't
panic on him. Not yet fall, where we
can see from the middle of the tracks
standing there with concrete feet the oncoming
locomotion, as all around us the little
omens of debris fall about our heads.
They are all poems, in my mind.
About winning touchdowns on cool nights
in Minnesota or Kansas. About the second
and third kisses of 14-year-olds that never
later, in young- or mid-adulthood, live up
to their full-lipped erotic promise.
They are about the childhood dog under
your bed you thought was just sleeping.
They are about difficult births.
They are about falling leaves,
which makes them about themselves,
and two of them slide down on air
into one another like two cars moving
into the same lane, whose collision becomes
a metaphor for the two seasons, or for two lovers:
one in an updraft she'd been caught in
since childhood when her father would
slap her cheek at the dinner table and
the other, he, still arcing down as if he's
in a swing, the stem of his little-boy-legs
out in front of him until he reaches that high
moment of suspense when the torso leans
back in childlike oblivion, the way his mother,
in his mind, tossed herself off that bridge,
backwards, and disappeared. No, not yet fall.
But the light's at a different slant, a different
attitude, shadows longer, and inside the heat
is a touch of something threatening itself,

felt beneath the skin, a foreshadowing
of sorts, of cool nights and of that long
sleep from whose depths no one
emerges groggy or rested.

Mark Weiss, photograph

## Justin Hamm

# *Rebekah Just When the Drought Was Ending*

But the best thing about Rebekah
was the way she floated always
beneath the scent of woodburn
and dusty Middle America,
her keen ranch-queen convictions
slicing deep and deeper into
the tiniest of daily miseries
with skepticism, demanding always
some proof before she'd concede
this life He pieced together for us
cell by cell with ever shakier Godfingers
contained even one malignancy.

Every bow-legged young bull rider,
every sunburnt farmer of someday
who stopped by to mend a fence
or just to offer genteel salutations
would see her backlit by sunset,
dream her into his own mother
and pray to the essence of the prairie
to do what old bones could not.
And it worked. She survived well enough
to give of herself four more seasons
among luckless kinfolk who every one
drank greedily the blood she squeezed
and felt the cracked lips of dry times less.

As long as there was some great need
into which she could empty herself
she could will the heart to continue
and none of the rules of dying applied,
but she must've seen that the new rain
wasn't baptismal or meant for her restoration.
When those stormclouds finally swelled
and burst into fat miracle drumbeats
she must've felt the change was coming on.
Why else open the windows so wide

with no thought for the evening chill?
Why else cut a hundred wildflowers
and arrange them into fiery clusters
but pour no water into their vases?

Jen Hoppa, photograph

# *Illinois, Route 3*

If this road could answer
I would ask her what it is like
to follow the path
of the rippleshimmery river
for too many miles
through the slowly ghosting towns
and the corncovered landscapes
of the dying Midwest
first through hills so subtle
they seem like mere rumors
and then through more
significant undulations
that rise up suddenly
like tumors—only to be abandoned
completely spent and alone
in some lesser Cairo
long before you could ever tune
your ear  to the lovely blue notes
of Memphis, Tennessee
or feel the tingling creepies
drifting out from the voodoo
niches of New Orleans

I would kneel down right here
where the darkness is thickest
and hides the sign that warns
*Danger: Falling Rock*
and I would listen as the one
tiny swath of pavement
glowing brightest white
under the sharp cuticle moon
speaks of its great envy
and the river pageants past
like so many onetime lovers
all arrogant momentum
all callous purpose
without the slightest
hint of hesitation

# *A Case for Insomnia*

Another night has come another hour
when the raccoon has sorted all the refuse,
when the flickering streetlight steadies
and black blooms out from its golden eye.

It is in this hour that you experience joy,
though perhaps not recognizing it
in the sidewalk beneath the trembling
of the dogwood as it combs light,
and shadow, shadow across your window.

A cup of tea is steeping, or maybe brandy
burns the throat. Maybe you have
risen from a bad dream,
shocked by the cold floor into waking. Maybe
you have risen at the sound of the street sweeper
alone in her bright machine, tracing the bones of the city.

And even if it is grief that lifts your head
from the pillow, a space left empty
beside you, you can still taste
the way the night holds everything in its mouth,
savored and cold like the ice
cube dropped into the glass with its perfect chime.

## Dian Duchin Reed

# *Identity Fraud*

We're all born in the center of the universe,
right from the beginning screaming
*me me me*. Mostly
we grow out of it with wobbly baby steps

though not everyone finds the seeds of selflessness
tucked into their genetic backpack.
There are a few who'll kill you for pocket change
and stick around to finish your burger and fries,

a few who'll steal your pension to furnish
their third mansion or fill their pool with greenbacks
instead of water. As counterweight to
the unredeemably selfish, I nominate Thomas à Kempis,

who once wrote the book on humility. *Abandon self,*
he urged his readers. *You must not think*
*you have made any progress until you look upon yourself*
*as inferior to all others*. The truth is,

I seem to be superglued to my
self. I dread losing track of my identity;
having it stolen would be bad enough,
but at least then I could blame somebody…

which reminds me of the two men who both believed
they were God. They met at the mental asylum
and had a nice chat. Later, one of them described the other as
nice enough, but the fool's under the delusion that he's Me.

Then there are those who have the Cotard delusion
and are certain that they're dead, despite the fact
that they can still walk around and tell their doctor about it.
What do we know? Each of us is a raisin

in the rising bread dough of humanity. To each raisin,
all the others appear to be moving away, while the self stands
still at the center, and this
despite Thomas' clue: *As you see others, so they see you.*

# *Illumination*

A ragged corona of yellow construction paper
around my face identified me as the Sun

in my first-grade play. At the time, illumination
meant the flashlight in my hand. Already

I was a character bound to the pages of life's book,
stuck in a plot of many twists. How I longed

to trade places with Baron Munchausen,
who escaped from the swamp he was stuck in

by pulling up on his hair and lifting. We all
long for something. Midas craved a golden

garden, and to Gilgamesh paradise looked like
carnelian fruits with lapis lazuli leaves.

It took years for me to realize that even pigeons'
necks gleam opal, emerald, amethyst. Clouds too

can float like happiness. The soft gray dove, sharp-
shinned hawk, and great hushed owl have honeycomb

skeletons lighter than their feathers, which allow them
to fly in the manner of moments: seemingly close

enough to touch, impossible to catch. The Monastery
of the Metamorphosis, perched high on its rock

pinnacle in Greece, reaches up to heaven yet
knows enough to keep its feet on earth.

# *Round*

Every time I see
this two-crowned
redwood tree, I frown,
sense I'm going round
in circles. Lost. A woman
on the edge, satellite
of someone else's sphere
of influence. Circles
are perfect, can't get
any rounder. Ptolemy
and Aristotle agreed
that's how planets
must wander, that's
why Dante went
through Hell in nine
downward circles
before he found
a perfect woman
to float him through
Heaven's nine spheres,
all fears forgotten.
I'm uncentered,
not perfect, bound
to the wheel of karma,
delicious circle around
which I row row row
my boat forever, never
arrive, although recycling
is no perpetual energy
machine—all of us
wound down
by entropy, surrounded.
Lost, not found.
Look, that tree again.

# *Flares*

All that is still and silent shouts,
sends up flares bursting
from the ruby throats

of house finches, prods
with the chip, chip
of the dark-eyed junco,

begs a look with flickers and light,
electric minnows turning fin on fin,
holly berries in lacquered ice.

Even hardwoods in winter, stripped
to gray, beckon, long lithe limbs
swooning us into the waltz.

These are songs you must not refuse.
Unheard and unattended,
they pour melancholy,

trudge like Russian winter
toward freezing, strike chords that
pinch the arteries feeding the heart,

string your body with the threat
of a coming dirge, whatever it takes
to make you listen for the sounds of being.

If you are still enough to hear
that which cannot be heard,
open as a reed,

you will become the instrument
and the joyful tune, the stillness
tugging at your sleeve.

## *Baise-Moi*

Expecting someone else,
her hair a rumpled mess,
she met me at the door
in the short, silk nightdress
she'd been sleeping in.
My breath taken away,
unsteady on my feet
from what I had been drinking,
I stepped back.
It was not what I was there for—
yet I could not help
taking her in my arms,
at first to feel the silk,
the small of her back,
then her bare shoulders,
and to kiss those lips
I had always wondered
what it would be like to kiss.

# *These Are the Days*

*Odalisque*

Waiting for the mail after coffee,
the cat fed, the paper read online;
nothing more to do than wander
the house, the yard,
in t-shirt and underpants—
she luxuriates in the lack
of obligation.
Knowing how few things
one really needs in this life,
how most people are there
just to waste your time,
she tries to decide between
*No vacancies here,*
and *Everything is vacant.*
The afternoon she'll spend
reading in bed, Flaubert or Simenon,
too hot to do anything else.
Come evening, the few friends
she lets in will bring wine,
and leave their shoes at the door.

Erica Lehrer, photograph

KRISTEN INGRID HOGGATT

## *Zarya's Lessons*

*Ulugbek, Uzbekistan*

Zarya taught me how to feed eggplant through a meat grinder,
how to moan with the Khazak woman giving birth in the back
of our house, as Zarya chanted verses from the Quran
to keep the child safe from the ill-willed movements of eyes.

Day after day, the crowds overflowed the courtyard, their offering jars
decorating the broken blue tiles: cabbage, *chisnok*, tomato and *tum*.
They had goiter, anemia, an uncle with TB, or the nameless fatigue
of the displaced, that would enter the ear with the evening call to prayer.

One October, a man's forearm trapped him in a cotton tractor for hours.
He screamed like a hungry child as Zarya wrapped his arm
in Chinese silk scarves and read the Quran in Cyrillic script,
the parts lost in translation provided in her song, for she knew loss

better than most, after the car's angry screech and the oncoming bright,
vodka's elapsing sixty degrees, after the coma and the death of her son,
Zarya chanted and the screaming eased. Did the room tremble
that autumn afternoon? Outside on graying limbs, leaves fought the fall.

The man left with *spasieba*—then *raxmat, xudoga shukur*,
parsley flakes and parts of lamb, his broken bones going back
to the *shokran* of old miracles. Zarya would say, "Love those
who've stolen from you," and "Don't drink water—drink tea,"

steeping sadness in a pot of green. One time, she told me
a story of a woman who found a persimmon tree that gave forth
fruit so soft and brown, she told the children it was chocolate,
and when the Russians came and brought real chocolate

the angry children threw the fruit at her house until piles surrounded
on all sides and she couldn't get out. Zarya told me that story
just before I left, as we were cutting onions in the dank kitchen
with poorly forged knives. The fumes from the onions made us cry.

## *Potion*

Iron, lead, pepper, dirt,
fetid curse of undone work.
Roasted bits of baby cowl,
stone coyotes, mason's trowel.
Sacred remnants in a bowl,
marble pestle, ground to soul.

## *Thinning*

A season of forgotten prunings lies reproachfully in the corner by the milking shed. Who will cart them to the trash pile? Obtain the burning permit from Lester, keeper of the matches? Donny Trueblood left with Carla yesterday, Gibson strapped across his shoulders, Marine Band shoved onto his hip. Girl has no idea what she's getting into, thinks her grandmother, who loved a picker in a day that still brings fire to legs too thin to care.

# *Taverna*

My bow of little rags doesn't symbolize
black ones. Bow of little rags?
"What do you mean by that?" Let's say a
lasso, let's say a net, that catches you and
makes you ask that question. As if you lit a smoke,
tunk, tunk, tunk, see how nicely it
burns. "That's cheap, dude,"
you don't need to invite anyone out to eat. Tak, tak,
yes, those are tiny little billfolds for communication.
A fishing pole for catching ones like you. Oops,
they fly off in the air and drop in the sea.
They smell of milk and mother's gel
and when you're big, you'll also be a famous writer.

*Translated from the Slovenian by Michael Biggins with the author*

# *Ptuj*

Refuse from a *tundula.*
The *caro anita* of mankind.
These are lions on a bridge without manes.
Stampless horses without bellies.
*Pupolotti* (bulbs) that burn out and get changed.
A real bridge with a real foundation, with real water, and a wet
shadow. What here can be walked across, we always swam.
Spinning our hats and stovepipes in the sea water.
Fashion doesn't grow old. Water doesn't grow old.
The turning point in the nest should be overpaid.
I remember you with knitting needles in your lap, when you used them
to point at Rafko.
A buck loped down from the castle.
Rosette, a rose, Rosika. Where Mazlu, Stancic
Avšic, Mrs. Abramic, and Mrs. Sencar (née Ban) gathered.
First wipe off the knife, then the grave.
The soldiers are marching off to sleep.

*Translated from the Slovenian by Michael Biggins with the author*

## Susan Elbe

# *In Which I Enter, not the Last Room, but the Hidden One*

This is the room I didn't know existed, the one
where abandon is meant, where
I wake brushing factory soot from my hair,
scrub the smell of night from my fingers,
the metallic taste of the moon from my tongue.

This is where I lift my heavy life, wrung
and still wet, hang it on the line,
come clean in the wind, where I return to wanting
to touch the rough doors, latches, and yes,
even the uneven floors, with almost tenderness.

This is where I don't get saved, but so close to it
my hair stands on end, where I wrap
my bloody knees and ice my black-and-blue,
where I accept the heart is neither fragile
nor indifferent, but street fighter to its core.

# *Kumārajīva writes, from the Western Heaven, to T. S. Eliot*

So, what's with this *shantih shantih shantih* shtick?
It doesn't work. I'll get around to that. But first ...

That day, I arrived with the others. Then as now,
The Great Ferries carried their passengers
Across the rivers. I hadn't imagined, when alive,
That death brings so many
To peace, to right intent, to right effort.
We look to each other, offer helping hands.

I asked, bewildered, why this Western Heaven,
The heaven of Ha-Shem, Adonai, the Holy Ancient One?
(You'll observe I don't write, or say, the Name.)
They said it was an "assignment error."
I thought they'd fix it, approve my request
For placement somewhere else. Another pure land.
I've been here sixteen hundred years.
I don't recall how long it's been since I pressed the issue.
Centuries. Centuries. Well over a millennium.

An error of assignment, a ticket to the wrong place,
Brought a blessing. I began to study Torah
With those who came before: Rabban Hillel, Shammai,
The tragic Eliezer, Rabban Gamaliel. All gone now,
Theirs the *prajna* of the farther shore. No one stays here.
Not forever. Who'd want to? The Christians,
With their fantasy of permanence,
Take a long time letting go of eternity.

*Prajna*—what word in English? What word
For the holy marriage of knowledge and compassion?
Wisdom, insight, intuition—laden with connotations.
Only attain it, the next assignment is your choice.
You can return to the world for others' sake.
Today, Eliezer welds sculptures in Cincinnati,

Goes to temple on Shabbat, argues with the rabbi,
Says, if your interpretation be true, let these walls prove it,
Says he's an atheist, because walls, trees, rivers
Say nothing about Torah. Says that's a good thing,
Because it means we decide,
Which is what Ha-Shem intended all along.

And I, the child of Jiva, my mother, king's daughter
From Kucha, beside the great desert,
And Kumarayana, my Brahmin father,
Who crossed the mountains at the top of the world;
I, traveler across borders, India to Kucha to China;
Translator of the sutras, Sanskrit to Chinese,
Of the *Prajnaparamita,* of the works of Nagarjuna;
Teacher, made National Teacher by the king in Changan;
How could I not stay? Right effort demanded I stay.
So much to learn. New languages, new thoughts.
So much to teach. Always translation's task.

Hebrew has a word, *hevel.* All is *hevel,* vanity, vapor, mist.
It also names the brother murdered by Qayin, the spearsmith.
Will that do for emptiness, *shunyata?* I am still not sure.

True correspondence, or not? Moses de Leon
Reads me shining words from the Book of Splendor:
"The soul of the soul is the Holy Ancient One.
All is connected, this one to that one." Is that
*Pratityasamutpada?* "What this is, that is"? Moses says yes.
Do our minds meet? Is his another way of saying
All things possess Buddha nature?
What have I become? A Jewish Buddhist, a Buddhist Jew?

Beside stream and lake and sea Moses and I walk arm in arm.
Sometimes we sense a third, someone walking with us,
Someone we cannot clearly see. Vairochana? Ezekiel? Gabriel?
The Holy Ancient One himself, who spoke with the first Moses
As friend to friend, face to face? Or someone else?

Then there are the poets, my friends, Walt and Miss Dickinson.
Always Miss Dickinson. We too walk arm in arm, and he recites,

"For every atom belonging to me as good belongs to you."
And she recites, "The abdication of belief / Makes the behavior small."
The other night we had to leave the bar—HURRY UP PLEASE—
We downed our last drinks, and propping each other up,
We stumbled home. And she said, enough of Miss Dickinson,
Call me Emily. And I said, I will. And she said, wild nights ahead.
Walt said, *Pratityasamutpada.* We are the symbol and the proof.
I said, eighty proof. Plus chaser. Boilermakers. He said, every atom.

And oh the music! When Trane first played *A Love Supreme,*
I wondered, is this more than noise? I've listened and listened again,
And now I think, yes, this too teaches the Dharma. This too.
Have you listened to his instruction? Even if you have,
You ought to come here, to hear Trane yourself, if you can.

Why am I here, and you wherever you are, Mr. Calabash?
There are Christians, ferry-loads of them, and even some saints.
The saint from Assisi is here, and Abelard, though he's not one.
And there are poets. Among the newer arrivals, a sad man
Who calls himself Henry, not his real name; may his sadness lift.
And another, so tender to his mother, crazed on earth, now healed.
It goes without saying, we no longer say the Kaddish
For those in the Western Heaven. Sometimes we say it for those
Who are lost, those still on earth.

I said your *shantih* spiel doesn't work. Now's the time to look into that.
Time for you. For me, it's getting close to closing time.
I'm learning to play the sax—better, to play jazz. Once, I practiced,
Practiced, and was proud to be note-perfect. Trane laughed,
And Bird laughed, and they said, give it time,
Give it time.
Time.
T ... T ... T ...
You'll warble like a mockingbird, not squawk like some old crow.
Thanks, I said. Then Bird said, you can play jazz with just one note.
And Trane said, music is silence.
To play jazz and not the imitation of jazz, listen for the silence.
It's in the timing.

I take my sax along, stand on the bank, and play
On the days the ferry leaves for the farther shore.
Someday the ferrymen will say, That's some playing,
Not the imitation of playing. That's *prajna,*
Not its translation.
Come aboard. Where should we drop you off?
And I will choose. But now, I write.

Firstly, for the spiel to work, you have to believe it, and you don't.
The Upanishads, the Tarot, the Fisher King—you don't believe them.
Walt wrote of the hermit thrush, believed what it said in its song.
The thrush helped him make a place in his heart
For the death of the powerful western fallen star.
But for you these are broken images you've tossed on the heap.
Leave them be. Leave them, for those who trust them.

Secondly, you are nostalgic for an age when cities were real.
Your nostalgia longs for an illusion. Right awareness, T. S.!
In my time, cities were as real as they are today, no more.
Recall this: Siddhartha and his wife, Yashodara, making love
On a roof so passionately they don't notice when they fall off.
So spiritual, will you say, so different from Albert and Lil?
All anyone has is this age, his age, her age. Whatever its size,
The cup brims over with salt sorrows and sweet joys.
Simeon the Just spoke of the world's three foundations:
"The Torah; the divine service; and deeds of loving-kindness."
Where's your loving-kindness, your *hesed*? One word, one deed.
Start with Lil—her Albert *is* a problem. And spare some
For Lou and May. The *Dharmakaya* lies in these as well as anyone.

Thirdly, your shoes pinch and the knot in your tie is pulled too tight.
Hence the dyspeptic tone and the *kvetching*.
You complain about a dead world, a waste land.
It's April on earth, and the cup of the earth fills
With lilacs blooming in the dooryards,
With redbuds on the edges of the woods in Indiana,
With apple blossoms in the orchards of Michigan and Washington,
With spring beauty, anemone, trillium, Dutchman's breeches
Among the oak leaves on the trembling ground in the woodlands,
With woodchucks trundling from their burrows,

With fox kits venturing from their dens and seeing the world.
And I, a kit, a child, I go forth every day,
And the first object I look upon, that object I become.

Emily dozes on the bed. Walt's cat is asleep on the window seat.
It purrs. *PRRR.*
*PRRR. Prajna.* Diving, soaring, into the soul of the soul. To see
*PRRR. Pratityasamutpada.* What this is, that is. All connected, this one and that.
*PRRR.* praise! praise! praise!—So sings the hermit thrush.

Erica Lehrer, photograph

# *In the Cotswolds to Mourn a Recent Loss*

There, in the lavender field at Snowshill
November's morning chill quickened our walk
Amid the browned-out scentless stalks, small clumps
Cut back to rounded tufts, 'til at row's end
Two ring-necked pheasants rose as one and took
Their flight across the fence we'd come along.

There, back in Stow, in the warmth of the pub's
Old fireplace we watched thin stalks of smoke
Curl and twist, drift, entwine, then lift again
In swirling rings as a barmaid stoked spent
Embers back. We talked of that November's
Letting go, and of next year's promised scent.

# *Intimate*

Seldom seen and not much loved,
at the bottom of it all, the soles of the feet.
Born with you, red and wrinkled,
those first ink prints so precious. Now
they're tired dogs, witnesses to every step.
Adored by no one (not even you, not really).
In extremity as far from the magnificent
brain and the heaving heart as it gets.

Not famous like your voice,
not nimble like your fingertips.
They love blindly the cool dew,
hot sand on the beach, the good touch
of the therapist, brand-new cushy boots.

Hardened travelers standing ground,
they keep time, a solitary rhythm.
Thick, leathery, neglected, humble;
First to learn of rough going.
Considered private by some,
they hide, self-conscious perhaps,
having taken you down the wrong road
awkwardly, and more than once.

*Here, take mine,* you offer,
as you slide out of your slippers
so I can get to the garage
for something I forgot.
I step in. Warmth rises, fills me,
burning with all that you are.

## *In the weeks after she died, I kept on walking*

To work daily, due east,
and back home, due west,
always with the sun in my eyes:

Morning:
The gritty remains of winter
rot in shaded ditches.
Sticking out of an ice mound
there's a raccoon, belly up, legs stiff.

Evening, up hill and down:
Oncoming car, backlit:
A small child rides toward me in shadow.
As if dressed for a party, she wears
a mask of gold, not burnished bright,
but soft, as if cast fresh from lost wax.

Another day, sun-blind and moving forward:
I catch sounds: engine of a propeller plane,
the cry of a mourning dove.
The shoulder of the road
glitters with sand and sharded glass.

Midday:
In a side yard eight little kids
giggle around a badminton net,
the shuttlecock missing.

Sunglasses:
Eyes on the road, everything sepia,
the periphery relentless with color.
Between shoulder and fence line,
fresh mounds of black dirt glisten
in the light, raised up
from green grass.

The raccoon is reduced now.
Fur like cattail fluff
floats on dark water.

And that afternoon:
Just ahead a small boy
crouches at the boulevard's edge,
intent on something:
a round glass in his hand,
a wisp of smoke rising.

Full spring now:
A leafless tree,
a strand of Christmas lights
forgotten in the branches—
I think of her—
catching the sunlight.

From the collection of the Editor, photograph

## DEBRA McCALL

# *Maps*

All day moving towards this space
a cup of tea, a chair in the sun
and the empty page
like a map inscribed in invisible ink
whose message surfaces upon contact
whether the words come from the tree
the paper's born of or electrical currents
channeled through the pen I am not sure
I only know when I open a place
in the center of the day
where rules are stripped by the wind
where breaths are not doled out
by the tick of a clock
answers slip in to unasked questions
how nothing is as it seems–
not the tea nor the chair
which now stand as sentries
to a mythic realm
nor this room where we meet
now a forest of light
and you and I, roadworn lovers,
become innocent children
intent on following the map between us
and the stories we spill become
breadcrumbs along the way
uncovering the treasure
that was already here.

# *Norteamérica*

The cartographer's pen splits water
from the earth. His nib
carves into paper the coasts
of what is known.

But when a gull presses out
beyond the bounding circle
of his vision, the line runs dry,
gives up its graphite ghost.

The old maps showed a continent
unclosed, a land not land, or conquered.
We pretended to be Adam,
naming New Mexico

into the borders of Apache land.
But also stole
much older sounds
left chewed in the mouth—

Manhattan: island
of the many hills.
Michigan: big water.
Twenty-five of fifty states.

I cannot pull apart this place,
these overlapping thoughts.
What canyons have I scarred
with speech,

destroyed by merely knowing?

## *Columbus Day Prayer*

There is no mail.
The discoverer breeds a silence

normally reserved for church:
Sabbath guilt and mumbled hymns.

Like all my thoughts,
a night wind sneezes through

a desiccated autumn,
—the wind is

puffing through the cross-hatched screen
of the window cracked open.

Indian summer has wandered
over Michigan.

I hear the insects
hoarsely singing, bowing

ugly violins. Arpeggios vibrate deep
in their limbs—like fitful dreams—

when I pull the sheet out
from corners—dreams where I am walking

through cities of garbage,
through thousands of magazine-clipped men.

I slalom through the streets,
an aimless bird stuffed with rags.

Left home—up and gone in the night
like a rapture.

The streets grid out
in all directions,

spreading their veins,
infected with desire,

pressing out over plains,
the plague of their cartography.

I am no road, no fence, no house,
but fields, which billow like a sheet—

and I remember riding once
a bus across the border into Turkey.

Unexpected sunflowers
leaning in a wind of amber

swelled out across my sight
and minarets like noble flowers

turned all their muezzin throats upward,
singing to me: turn

& may God fall down on you—
turn & may God

fall down on your hands like light.

# *Map Song*

*Australia's indigenous peoples use songlines, which are song cycles passed down from the Spirit Beings, to navigate vast terrain and identify sacred landmarks.*

I.

First you should know
you can sing your way back.

Say you've rounded a bend
you don't recognize—

Say the thread of trail you're on
disappears.

Terrain wells up around you
becoming a trap
or a puzzle.

Mountains blur and collapse,
losing their names.

The twist of the river
suggests nothing;

there is no pattern
in the trees.

II.

I know a people
who embed their maps in song.

They sing their way back,
as the landscape balks—
as it veils itself in shadow and light.

The song is a relic,
it leads to the ridgeline—
it rises up and knows where it's going.

III.

Ahead, there are signs we can't distinguish,
the earth waits to be known.

We keep singing.

Kathleen Kemarre, Woodcut print from Utopia Suite

# *Urban Surrealism*

I don't have a picture of that day. It was November—the caprice of wind
was lifting off hats and whipping cyclones of leaves. All day we knelt
on the difficult macadam, which stretched between a fence and the
nondescript school. We painted a masterpiece, section by section,
a hued patchwork in negative space so that only in stepping back from the work
could we see what we made—an easy metaphor—but then this:
the kids working beside me. And what could be given them, really,
they did not already possess? What metaphor for their existence,
impotent brush strokes that should have been singing?
There isn't time for past tense, I know. There is only this purple octopus below us,
with its limp and graceful arms, and the Ben Franklin Bridge
disproportionately small. There is the skyline, Dalí-like,
dwarfed by an abstract sun and a clump of seaweed waving in one,
unchanging tide. There is this girl, this boy beside me.
There is the picture I did not take. And there is and there is not enough time.

## *John Keats, on Meeting Leigh Hunt*

*An era in my existence,* he called it,
that October morning Keats walked
the five miles from Clerkenwell to meet him.
I imagine his quickened step, his audible
breath as he approached the Vale,
the whitewashed cottage where Hunt lived among
prints of mythic scenes and busts of heroes.
Kindly Leigh Hunt, mover and shaker among painters
and poets and large thinkers of Liberal mind;
such conversational eloquence
they must have exchanged; such clasping
of appreciative hands.
Though Keats would eventually surpass him
by light-years, for now, there was this first
meeting as of two great constellations—imagine
the fierceness and reach of such light.

# *On Viewing Caravaggio's* The Conversion of St. Paul, *1601, Santa Maria del Popolo, Rome*

At first all you notice is the hefty body
of the horse, and under its raised leg, a man
sprawled on the ground, overcome
by a vision that has wrenched away his control,
sword dropped at his side, eyes shut
and arms upraised—see how the light
holds on to his outstretched hand,
how he is left—as the viewer is—
in the shock of this light, all else deep
in shadow, even the people behind you
all herded to this spot, to be struck
by this moment
that has not stopped shining.

# *Alphabet of the Fish*

from *Alphabets of Desire & Sorrow*
*A Book of Imaginary Colophons**

Among the clouds, a fish pursued indolently its occupations at the bottom of a reflecting pool where pilgrims to the Tombs of the Three Emperors stopped to feed with crumbs the carp—their red, black, and gold skins like tongues of fire no ordinary waters have power to extinguish. Kuroda Seiichi, who once had walked with the poet Bashō as far as the Western Hills, likened them to thoughts in the mind of Buddha—shining and indifferent to the world of men, which is nonetheless thought's realization. Kuroda's 1697 poem "Fish Among Clouds" (its ideographs on mulberry paper, said to have been deliberately smudged) is interpreted by some scholars of the Edo period as an expression of divine absence while others insist that its illegibility conceals a presence too dazzling for mortal eyes.

*Like one of Joseph Cornell's mysterious boxes, each "alphabet" is a theatre sufficient unto itself and, simultaneously, an evocation of a lost history. I use remnants of vanished sciences, traditions, languages and beliefs to build a composition in the way Max Ernst appropriated old engravings or took rubbings from the natural world. The result—it is to be hoped—is a work whose purpose is more than aesthetic pleasure. To quote one of Rikki Ducornet's narrators: "I write from the new century about the old, my purpose to reanimate planets that have long ceased to spin."

## Michael Boccardo

# *Edward Hopper's* New York Movie, *1939*

Even with her eyes averted, sheathed
inside her hourglass of light, she still sees them,
the lovers, fumbling iridescent against the screen.
For a moment, she ponders their bodies—
fevered, impatient—unlike the way she would ponder
her own, his fingers like vines climbing the trellis
of the woman's zippered gown, their moans muffled,
gauzed in fog. Instead, she begins to picture
their future: marriage, a son, daughter, a house fenced
with the drowsy advice of tulips,
when against a folded arm she suddenly notices the weight
of each breast, pendulous through her uniform, how
they lie almost like strangers, side by side, somber
under a rivet of mottled buttons. But soon the final scene
will silver toward a darkness in which she's left
to only imagine the rest, her heart a vacant seat
among an audience who hardly stir. Not the man
with hair as slick as burnished iron, or the woman, slouched
rows ahead, loneliness tipping the brim of a hat low
over her powdered face, both of them reticent,
both rooted to desires already growing as dim as the glow
from the usherette's angled torch, its flicker like the quickest
of moths, dusting the edges of rails, brass winking,
surviving long enough to slip between a curtain's gilded cords.
Upstairs, she hears the shuffle of another audience,
tickets shorn, shoes scuffing the lobby floor loud
as the slap of a projection reel. Like them, she longs
for the slow striptease of darkness, for chairs to unfold
their rigid spines, and shadows, infinite
along the walls, to shinny loose, lie like careless pools
of stockings at her feet, while she eagerly slips again
inside a different life, one she knows will leave her eyes liquid,
shimmering, a mirage she always mistakes for weeping.

# *Woman of the Year: A Gay Man's Meditation on Marriage*

I'm sitting in a classroom watching the death of a lesbian vampire. The Countess is lying in her open casket, motionless, her eyes wide. Standing over her is the hero—tall, muscular, sure of his vitality. He places the stake against the Countess's chest and hammers it into place. The Countess spreads her lips and hisses. On the other side of the crypt, her human bride, a wispy femme with two red spots on her neck like beauty marks, releases a sympathetic howl as her vampire lover crumbles to dust.

Watching the hero take the femme in his arms and kiss her, the "all is well" music so loud it makes the speakers buzz, I begin to put my thoughts together for the post-screening discussion. This is what I'll say:

"A friend of mine called me earlier this week. It was the day the California Supreme Court okayed gay marriage and she was ecstatic, went on about the birthing of a new era, about taking her girlfriend to this 'Promised Land' and tying the knot. When she asked what I thought, I responded the way I thought she wanted me to, saying how fantastic it all was. But really, I was unsure, and now I think I know why. The Countess is dead not because she was evil, but because she wanted to be human, because she thought the only way for her to be with the woman she loved was to make her her bride. Aren't we doing the same thing? Aren't we being fooled to think acceptance comes only by assimilation, transforming ourselves into 'man' and 'wife'? Are we forgetting our vampire ways?"

But by the time my professor calls on me, my thoughts have stopped making sense. I can't be sure if it is the fact that the Countess wants to marry a woman or the fact that she falls in love in the first place that brings about her demise.

* * *

I was eighteen years old when Roger asked me to marry him. I had been out for a year and was still learning—what to wear, how to speak, where to be seen, how to kiss a boy, how to give a blowjob. Now that I was away from my hometown of Dayton,

Ohio, free from all of the lessons on boy/manhood I'd been reared with, I was able to breathe in and adapt to this new world. It didn't occur to me then that I might be simply exchanging one set of social norms for another. I was a young gay man, I had my first boyfriend, and I was ready to explore this identity.

We'd been dating for six months, since the summer following my high school graduation, before my first semester at film school. Film had been an obsession of mine since childhood. Through my awkward early teen years, I studied Tim Burton, enthralled, however subconsciously, by his queer sensibilities, watching small towns try and fail to assimilate such strange, sexually ambiguous beings as Pee-wee Herman and Edward Scissorhands. In high school, I turned my attention to horror films. I identified with those monsters; those repressed "Others," watching with almost sadistic pleasure as they brought mayhem to the suffocating "normality" around them. By the time I finished high school, film school seemed the only appropriate move. I was enthusiastic, ready to make movies my solitary love. Then I gave Roger my phone number and became distracted.

Roger was twenty and had been out for most of his life. I was in awe of his experience, his understanding of gayness. I was captivated by his combination of delicate gestures and nerve; he'd bluntly asked for my number at Hops Bar and Grille while serving me potato skins. I looked forward to our "tutorials": "No, not like that. Like this. Feel that? It really accentuates your orgasm. Yeah, good. Now you're getting it. Oh, and you might want to trim a little down there. Don't you have an electric razor?"

I think he liked me for my incipience, for my naiveté. I was fresh. I lacked all of the baggage he'd associated with growing up queer—"Not even an illicit after-swimming, teenage rendezvous with a neighbor boy?" He could desert his history and start over again with me.

Roger studied musical theater back home in Dayton, and I drove the two hours every weekend to see him. Those drives were magical, always at night on meandering, frequently foggy back roads, the ever-present danger of wandering deer sprouting from the darkness into my headlights. This was romance. I would sit back in my seat, listen to the mix CDs he'd made for me, think about the scar on his cheek that he'd gotten from a car accident when he was a kid—a straight vertical line running from his cheekbone to his jaw like permanent red marker, the scar that embarrassed him and defined him at the same time, the scar that stretched when he smiled.

One Wednesday evening, after a class on Femme Fatales in Film, I decided I couldn't wait for the weekend. I jumped in the car and headed for home, headed for my boyfriend's bed (though "home" and "bed" belonged to the same town, I always considered these destinations completely separate). I imagined the surprise on his face when I arrived. This was the night he proposed to me.

He'd purchased the ring only a week before and was planning to wait until Christmas, maybe Valentine's Day. But then, there I was, in the middle of November—could this be fate? He took me to the playground behind his apartment building, to a tiny wooden pretend truck that didn't have wheels or doors, stuck in the middle of a sandbox. Roger held an imaginary door for me, and I squeezed into a space meant for someone half my size. In the driver's seat, Roger told me about his life, starting with his younger years, helplessly picked on in school for being "girly." There were other stops along the way, memories like landmarks, some good (his first on-stage performance in the chorus of *Little Shop of Horrors*), some not so good (his parents' response to his coming out: silent for a moment, then they changed the subject to the Monica Lewinsky scandal and never brought it up again). Then we arrived at this new stage of Roger's life: his acceptance into a musical theater program, the beginnings of his singing career, our meeting in a dingy bar and grille. At this point, Roger got out and walked to my side of the truck. As I stood to stretch my legs back out, he knelt down before me and offered up the ring.

I wasn't prepared for this moment. I didn't know fully what it meant, Roger being the one kneeling. Did this make him the man and me the woman? Had I always expected to be the one to kneel? To propose? And then there was Roger's face, looking up at me, waiting, his eyes wide and tearful, his lips forming a cautious grin, his scar stretched. I tried to imagine what he'd do if I said I'd think about it.

But what did I need to think about? Wasn't this always the goal? To find someone to love and start a life together, the way my parents had, the way my straight friends were doing? One of my high school girlfriends was eighteen and engaged. I'd thought she was too young for such a decision, but maybe I'd been jealous. She had a man, a wedding to plan, a house to build, a future. I had the movies.

So, even though I knew I wasn't finished learning how to be gay, I said yes to Roger's proposal. Whatever there was I still needed to know, he could certainly teach me.

* * *

The summer before I left for film school, I spent a lot of time in my parents' basement, in what we called the "Extra Room." It was a space where belongings and relics of questionable necessity were haphazardly stored, all spilling from overturned bins and cardboard boxes that were labeled for contents they no longer held. As if afraid I was leaving too much behind, I sifted through these piles of history, looking for old treasures that I might want to take with me to school.

In a box marked "Tax Papers," I discovered the early life of my parents as a couple: yearbooks, black-and-white kissing pictures from photo booths, old postcards, love letters. I opened one of the letters (addressed to my father's dorm room at Ohio State University, the return address Columbian High where my mother was completing her senior year), irrationally expecting to find poetic, lyrical prose, language my parents had never used in front of me, language that could only be inspired by young love. What I found instead resembled more the kinds of notes teenagers pass to each other in the classroom.

The letter began with my mother stating how bored she was in class and bragging about a few good test grades, then moved on to play practice and drama in general, her love of the stage, her excitement for opening night. It concluded with my mother looking forward to the next time my father would come home so they could make love. There was never much detail about making love in the letters, only that it was romantic and made my mother feel more in love.

As I went through the letters, all from my mother, I found that they were all variations of the same message. That is, until around number twenty, when my parents became engaged. Suddenly my mother was looking forward not to their next lovemaking, but to their wedding day, set for the summer. She spoke of her new class schedule, dropping math and science for home ec and bookkeeping, something her other engaged girlfriends were doing so they could get secretarial jobs after graduation to help put their soon-to-be husbands through school. One letter expressed my mother's slight regret, as if an afterthought, for not auditioning for the spring musical; she had been the lead in the last three plays. She said it was better that she get an after-school job and start saving money for their life together.

I didn't know what musical it was that she'd turned down, but in my head it was *Funny Girl,* and my mother would have been Fanny Brice, forced to choose between Omar Sharif and the stage—you can only have one!

When I became engaged, I wanted to ask my mother about this time in her life, about the role she was taking on, if she really wanted it or if she thought it was expected. Or both. I wanted to know what she thought her life would look like before she met my father, before the engagement. But then, I didn't want to intrude, didn't want to stir up old resentments, if there were any. And maybe there was a small fear in me that, once I opened my mother to the idea of the life she had not led, she would take me by the arm, pull me close, and tell me not to go through with it.

I'd looked everywhere for letters from my father during that time. I never found them. But I did find one more envelope, bulkier than the rest, holding something thicker than paper inside. I opened it and pulled out a cassette tape. "Possible Wedding Songs," was scribbled onto the label. I searched the Extra Room and found an old cassette player. I plugged it in, inserted the tape, listened to my eighteen-year-old mother— "And the songbirds are singing like they know the score. And I'll love you, I'll love you, I'll love you like never before—" trying her best to imitate Christine McVie's melancholy voice.

* * *

The ring was a simple band, white gold. At the center, a small diamond was embedded, framed by two horizontal strips rising from the ring like brackets, or tiny barricades.

I was embarrassed by the ring. It didn't look particularly feminine, but I knew what it meant, my wearing the ring of another man, and I was afraid of others knowing what it meant as well. Whenever I was in public, I did my best to keep my left hand hidden. I paid cashiers with my right hand, handed tickets to ticket-takers with my right hand. When I spoke, I gesticulated with my right hand. I used my right hand to shake others' right hands—which isn't unusual, but I was suddenly much more aware of it.

Every so often, someone would notice and ask about the ring, usually women. The one I remember most was Emma, a girl in my comp class, a pretty stranger who gave me the same nervous feeling, the same sweaty armpits and self-doubt, as did those girls I tried to date in high school. I'm not sure why I was so smitten; I wasn't attracted to her, at least not sexually. It was as though, having only recently come out, I still hadn't extinguished my need to be desired by women, to be an eligible candidate. Whatever the reason, I wanted Emma to like me. I wanted her to be attracted to me.

Emma sat in front of me in class so we were frequently paired up for group work, and in one of those sessions I must have forgotten about my left hand. It was not under my desk or shoved in my pocket; it was lying on top of my notebook, out in the open, flaunting the ring.

"What's that?" Emma asked.

"Oh," I said, jerking my hand to my chest reflexively, then, as if realizing I'd been caught, slowly placing my hand back onto the desk. "I'm engaged."

"Really?" Emma looked confused. And I knew why. "Does she have a ring, too?"

"Well," I said, surprised at how difficult this was to say, "I'm engaged to a man."

I must have averted my eyes, because I do not remember her expression at that moment. I'd probably thought it would be heavy with sudden judgment, and so I looked down. I imagined her, and everyone else in the world, thinking, *What right did two men have even to sleep together, much less get married?*

I was embarrassed also in simply being so young. I recalled the pity I'd had for my high school friend when she showed me her ring, and the pity I'd had for my young mother when I read her letters, a pity for the bitter complacency I'd imagined, and the regret, the lives unfulfilled. What did I think I was doing, getting married at eighteen? What did I know about life yet? Or love?

But I do remember, when I looked back up at her, the smile on Emma's face, and her saying, "Neat," before we went about answering the questions on our worksheet. I remember thinking how generous that gesture was, and asking myself what I'd been so worried about.

Perhaps I'd been embarrassed because I hadn't fully committed to the ring, to what the ring represented. Maybe it wasn't the ring at all. Maybe it was me—I didn't match the jewelry.

So I set about making alterations:

• I pierced my ears. What could better complement the ring than more jewelry?

• I changed my clothes. My best friend Krystal, with her keen eye for fashion, took me shopping, forced me into fitting rooms with pairs of tight jeans, tight, bright-colored shirts, blazers, belts, designer shoes that made my size-twelve feet look slender, almost dainty. When Roger saw me dressed like this for the first time, he removed my new clothes slowly and made love to me. I felt like I knew what it was to be a straight woman, having to carefully assemble her appearance to either attract or hide from the gaze of men.

• I grew my hair out, which took a bit more time. I bought a curling iron and lots of hairspray. I put waves in my hair that made me think of a picture I saw of my mother when she was my age.

• I worked out, not to build muscle, but to slim down. I wanted my waist as narrow as possible, to accentuate the breadth of my chest (which was slighter, I felt, than the chests of most men) and the curve of my ass (which I really didn't have).

• I walked differently. I practiced a runway strut in the small space of my dorm room when my roommate wasn't there, and I performed a tamer version of it in public, my head high, my neck long, my arms hardly leaving my sides, my hips swaying. I imagined straight men turning to look at my ass in tight jeans, forgetting momentarily that I was not a woman, or maybe not even caring.

This was a difficult task, trying to be the woman in our couple, as Roger could not pass as straight himself. He was loud about his sexuality, constantly making jokes of his lack of manhood, imitating black drag queens with his voice, jumping on stage to play queer role after queer role.

Yet *I* was the one wearing his ring. *I* had to make this work.

So, though I did as much as I could with my body and my affectations, I also made considerable concessions on the vocational front. We agreed that, after we got married, I would drop out of school and follow him to New York City, where he would build his career as a singer/dancer/actor. These did not feel like concessions at the time; the thought of running away from my past life, of completely submitting myself to this new identity, was intoxicating. I would work for temp agencies to support him and, someday, when he made it big, stay home to raise the kids. When compared with the idea of sitting in a dark editing room cutting and taping film strips to create the illusion of other lives being lived, this didn't only feel exciting: it felt right.

* * *

Krystal never said she didn't approve. She didn't need to. On the night of the proposal, just hours after I accepted the ring, I had Roger drive me across town to Krystal's parents' house. She met me out on the front lawn, and when I showed her the ring she could only stare at it as if it were a tattoo she couldn't interpret, a tattoo I couldn't remove. I felt the need to defend myself, but there was nothing in the air. No words. Then Roger stepped out of the car, walked up behind me. Krystal rolled her eyes, lifted her arm and said, "Well, come here," and gave him a hug.

I was grateful, then, for her silence, for her refusal to tell me what I should or shouldn't do. She had been that same quiet, consoling friend when we were in high school plays together, when she would patiently listen to my family troubles, my coming-out troubles, my boy troubles (or rather, lack of boy troubles) in the dark, empty dressing room. I can still see her face in the mirror, surrounded by scattered costumes and makeup kits, watching me with the avid joy of one being included, of one being needed.

But now I wonder if I'd needed something else from her—to hear that dissenting opinion, out loud. My parents, though they weren't likely overjoyed at the prospect of my early marriage, tried their best to be supportive of the lifestyle I'd chosen, and so said nothing negative. My married and engaged friends were thrilled that I was joining them in matrimony, happy to have their own choices affirmed, though maybe they, as I had, were simply attempting to fit Roger and me into comfortable roles, automatically branding one of us the husband, the other the wife, not to make the act of marriage between two men palatable, but simply to make sense of it, to assign names to the ambiguity they must have felt about me, or within me, as an eighteen-year-old who had decided a few months ago he was different.

No one spoke to me of these things. No one knew how to take up that role, to question. The closest Krystal ever came to contesting my would-be marriage was an excited phone call a week after I'd accepted Roger's proposal.

"He smokes," she said to me. I could tell from the overpowering hum in my ear that I was on speakerphone and that she was driving, though I'm not sure that's the reason she was yelling.

"What?" I said. I instinctively turned down the volume on my cell phone so that students and professors walking by wouldn't overhear.

"He smokes. Roger smokes. I just saw him. Cigarettes."

"Where did you see him?"

"In his car. He was sitting there, next to me at a stoplight, looking for a CD or something, cancer stick hanging out of his mouth." She waited for my response.

I wasn't sure what to think of it. I had never seen Roger with a cigarette. I wasn't sure what that would even look like.

"Did you know about this?" Krystal said.

It sounded like something someone should know about the person he or she was engaged to, so I said, "Yes."

Krystal was quiet for a moment. I imagined the same expression she'd worn that night in her front yard. Defeat. "Okay," she said, her voice deflated. "Didn't know if you knew."

I couldn't stop thinking about that cigarette. I thought about Roger smoking, how he stood when he smoked, who he talked to when he smoked, how he sounded when he talked when he smoked. Did he hold the cigarette between his forefinger and thumb? Let it bob up and down between his lips? Where did he smoke besides the car? Bathrooms? Underneath fire escapes in dark alleys with other smokers? I thought of all the men and fellow smokers he might be fucking. I thought about his hand smoothing chests, unzipping flies, stroking dicks. I stopped eating from fear of throwing up. I couldn't sleep. I began to feel like I did when I was a kid, watching horror movies on TV, turning the channel at the scary parts but turning right back, needing to see what was happening.

I brought it up the following weekend, the second I got home. I hugged him and asked, "Do you smoke?"

He looked at me, as if deciding whether or not to lie. "You smell it on me?"

I couldn't, but it seemed like something a fiancé should be able to detect. "Yes," I said.

He'd been smoking since he was fifteen. He said he was ashamed of it, along with many other things he did before we met. He said he wanted to be a better person for me, to put a stop to those old habits so he would feel deserving of me, and of marriage. He kissed me, said he would quit and don't worry. I said, "Okay," but I really wanted to ask, "What were those many other things?"

I would eventually find out that Roger could easily handle a twelve-pack of beer, that he used to smoke pot in the high school parking lot and tried coke once at a party, that he'd had about fifty sexual partners before me, including one threesome. "But that didn't really count," he said, "because I couldn't get it up." This didn't make me feel any better. When I asked if I was his first virgin, he laughed.

Roger didn't quit smoking, of course. So I started.

* * *

Now, I hardly ever look at the films I've made, but back in college, whenever I felt unsure of myself, regarding filmmaking or otherwise, I returned to those old high school projects, the ones I'd made with friends. Not long after Krystal's cigarette sighting, I pulled out a video Krystal and I had made for our senior English class about the Hollywood love story of Katharine Hepburn and Spencer Tracy.

I watched the two of us in pixilated black and white, costumed to look like those classic stars, performing dueling monologues that chronicled the affair. I had sprayed my hair white and painted wrinkles into my forehead. Krystal wore one of her mother's power suits and a brunette wig atop her head that we'd found at Foy's Costume Shop. The brown hair looked unnatural against Krystal's pale skin and blond eyebrows.

As we, the Hepburn/Tracy lookalikes, discussed the nine Hollywood films we'd made together, the video cut to reproductions of selected movie moments. The most striking to me, as I sat re-watching, was the final scene from *Woman of the Year* in which Hepburn, too successful and career-driven to be domesticated, tries to make breakfast for her husband, Tracy.

I watched myself as I sat at the table, glaring at Krystal over my morning paper. I watched Krystal scramble about the kitchen as if navigating a room she'd never been in before, watched her fail to operate the coffeemaker, pull the toast from the toaster black and shriveled, watched as I stood from my spot at the table, walked over to Krystal, took her in my arms, and kissed her.

Seeing the two of us interacting, playing husband and wife, I thought how much easier it would be if I could marry Krystal, a friend, not a lover. I wondered what kind of love marriage was supposed to be based on anyway. If romance and desire only lead to insecurity and doubt, jealousy and questions, maybe that kind of love is simply too volatile, incompatible with marriage. Do you have to be friends to make a marriage work? Did I even consider Roger a friend? Were we better off fulfilling our present desires and then parting ways when it grew tedious?

I would think these thoughts until the agony of never kissing Roger again trumped them.

* * *

Roger and I would frequently go on double dates with his older brother Alex and Alex's boyfriend/fiancé, Topper. Upon our first meeting, I immediately deduced which was the "man" and which the "woman."

Alex was the shorter of the two, but he had a muscular build and worked as a landscape architect for his father's company. He spoke softly, but precisely, and only when he had something important to say. Like most of the men in my own family, he was the breadwinner, the one who watched the finances, the one who made decisions like where to eat and what movie to see. He would be the husband. Topper was tall and slender, and he tucked his button-down shirts into his low-rise jeans, accentuating the feminine curve of his waist. He spoke loudly with a light lisp and a heavy southern accent, never with certainty, always flitting about his subjects. He told me that he wanted to be an actor, that he'd had a brief stint on a reality show and gotten a lot of attention from it, interviews for gay magazines, thousands of hits on his website. Just like Fanny, I thought. Just like my mother, giving up the business for her man. Topper would be the wife.

One night, Alex and Topper invited us to their duplex for dinner. When we arrived, only Alex was there, busy cooking. He told us to have a seat in the living room and brought out a tray of cheese and two glasses of wine. I thought how strange it was that Alex should be the one to do this, to serve us, to chat about the flavors in the wine and the different types of cheeses. This is something my father would never have done, unless it was a joke. But then again, I don't think my mother would either—she never served, but would simply set out the fixings like a buffet and let people have at it.

Shortly after, Topper came home, apologizing for being late: "Something went haywire at the office."

"Office?" I asked.

"The LGBT center," Topper said. He told us he was the head of their activity-planning department, and that he also ran a youth group for gay and lesbian teenagers. I wanted to know how much money he made, if it rivaled Alex's income, but I didn't ask.

"Did Alex give you the tour?" Topper asked. We said no. Topper looked at Alex through the kitchen doorway. "What kind of housewife are you?"

As Topper showed us around the cozy, young-couple living room, paying particular heed to its centerpiece—his DVD collection which consisted mostly of old slasher movies that Alex hated—I began to think I was being too narrow in my search for the perfect wife model. Here was Topper who seemed to be easily balancing his career with his home life; not only was he able to maintain his individuality, but he was proud of it, proud of his horror film collection. I had yet to come out to Roger as a horror-lover, afraid he'd think it was a perversion. Whenever he came to visit me at school, I made sure my collection was stashed away, deep in the closet.

The last place Topper showed us on the tour was their master bedroom. In the doorway, he said something I'll never forget, something that unsettled me, even knowing it was a joke. "This is where we try to make babies."

Roger and I talked about kids only once. I was in one of my dorm's closet-sized study rooms, where I went to phone Roger so my roommate would not overhear. The wooden chairs in the rooms were uncomfortable, so I lay on my back with my feet propped up against the wall. Roger told me about being in the delivery room earlier that day when his best friend, Maura, gave birth to her son. He told me how remarkable it was, and how he wanted that experience for himself.

"You want to give birth?" I joked.

"No," Roger said. "I want to have my own baby."

"Oh," I said. I waited for him to explain, and when he didn't I said, "How would that work?"

"I think Maura would do it," he said. "Carry it for me."

"Really?" My thoughts went again to Roger's smoking, to the things I couldn't visualize about his past, who he'd been, and now, who he wanted to be. I told him I wanted to adopt. It was selfish of him, I said, to want his own biological son or daughter when there were kids who needed homes—why else have two dads? At the time, I was convinced of this position; I believed it. I was not honest enough with myself to know that I was uncomfortable with the idea of someone else, some other woman, having Roger's baby, that I was ashamed of the fact that I could not give him one myself, that, yet again, I did not fit the mold.

* * *

Roger's oldest brother, Craig, and his wife, Dana, had had their house built a year ago, a two-story mini-mansion outside Cincinnati that I remember now as being completely beige, the beige of a Show Home. Roger and I (three months into our engagement) were staying with them for the weekend of Alex and Topper's union ceremony. I was afraid to touch things, though nothing looked particularly fragile. Just neat. The opposite of cozy. And spacious, too spacious for two people, I thought. I felt as though Roger and I would be sent to the basement, to some playroom for children where we'd be more at home and wouldn't disturb the tranquility of the upper floors. But Dana, petite and energetic, took us up to the guest bedroom. As she showed off the new shower curtain in the guest bathroom, along with the matching towels and washcloths in the linen closet, I wondered what was so different between this married couple and Alex and Topper, or Roger and me. I wondered if I would have matching towels in my linen closet.

I'd asked Roger once if there was any specific marriage he'd want to emulate, and he said, without a doubt, Craig and Dana. For the longest time, the background image on his computer was a photo of their wedding, the attractive couple shoving white cake into each other's mouths, Roger laughing and adoring them in the background.

We didn't know, just then, that Dana had been sleeping in this guest bedroom for the last three months, what would be the final three months of their two-year marriage. We didn't know that, once Dana left us to get settled, she would jump in her car and drive to a friend's place for the weekend, maybe longer. For all we knew, for all Roger knew, Craig and Dana were "it."

After we unpacked, I stretched out onto the bed. "This feels like a hotel room," I said. "Except nicer. My family always stayed at Red Roof Inns."

Roger stretched out next to me. "I want a place like this someday," he said.

I looked at him. This was the last place I ever imagined calling a home, but Roger was thinking about our future together, so I smiled and I kissed him, conveniently disregarding the "I" in his statement.

* * *

I took notes in my head as I sat in the second row, watching the ceremony: *Nice location. We should get married somewhere like this. No, I don't want my officiant wearing a rainbow sash. I like that the groom's men and women aren't uniform, though. But I hate the poinsettias, makes me think of office Christmas parties.*

Roger was already up front, standing next to the other wedding party members. There had been no grand entrance, no promenade down the aisle. It was simple, unpretentious. And when the time came, Alex and Topper walked the short walk to the front of the room, hand in hand. I liked that they entered together, neither one expressly the bride. Which side was it that the bride traditionally stood on?

I tried to look at Roger's face during the ceremony, but his back was turned to me; he was focused on the central action. When it came time for him to sing, I was ready with a smile that said "we're next," hoping he would look at me, would sing the song to me, at least one line. But his eyes remained forward as he sang to his audience.

Halfway through the reception, I found myself sitting at a table with an aunt and uncle. I tried to keep up my end of the conversation, but I spent most of the time watching Roger, drunk on the dance floor, laughing and hollering, grinding his body against Dana and other men and women I didn't know. I imagined grimy gay bars where Roger showed up in mesh shirts and eyeliner, drinking, smoking, snorting, dancing in cages and looking for someone, maybe two or three someones, to hook up with in the bathroom.

This is who Roger had been, I thought. This is who he wanted to be, a creature of perpetual night, and he couldn't be that person with me. I knew nothing about the gay scene. I knew nothing about sex. One of the only times I'd ever been in a bar, I ordered a rum and Coke and was embarrassed when the bartender asked me what kind of rum and I didn't know any labels. I didn't know how to be the kind of partner Roger needed. I didn't know if Roger needed a partner at all.

We argued in the car. I yelled at him for ditching me, for leaving me to sit alone with strangers while he made an ass of himself. He yelled at me for yelling at him on the night of his brother's wedding—wasn't he allowed to have a good time? I told him he smelled like alcohol as if it were the worst sin, and then came the thought: He doesn't fit either.

When we got back to the house, we found Craig in the kitchen, sitting alone on a stool, his elbows on the counter. He was rolling an empty beer bottle back and forth between his hands.

Roger sat on the stool next to his brother. He asked him if anything was wrong. He leaned in so close, I thought he might reach out and touch him, and even though he was his brother, I felt immediately jealous.

"Where's Dana?" Roger asked.

Craig shrugged. "Don't know," he said. The way Roger tilted his head forward, the way all the concerned crinkles in his face smoothed over—that same expression I saw in the junior high class photo his parents kept on the mantel, Roger sitting in the corner, unsmiling, next to his classmates but somehow not a part of them at all—told me he knew what was coming even before Craig said what he said next. "It's not going to work out."

Roger stared at his brother's feet, bare on the bottom rung of the stool. He didn't look like he wanted to touch him anymore. Then Roger stood up, walked toward me, walked past me, and went upstairs.

I found him in the guest bathroom. He was sitting on the toilet, his head between his knees, weeping. I'd heard Roger cry before, but this sounded different. These sounds were weightier. I didn't need the benefit of retrospection to know what he was feeling. I knew then. He wanted out. He wanted out before we built a house together.

I sat on the floor next to him and put my hand on his leg. I let him cry for a while, what then felt endless, like nothing else would ever follow, but now seems a mere snapshot, a frame removed from a filmstrip. I tried to get him to speak, to tell me what he was feeling, but all he was finally able to say was that he wanted to go outside for a cigarette. When I asked if I could share one with him, he said no.

The next morning, I felt guilty for the things I'd said to Roger in the car and wanted to make it up to him. I went downstairs while he was still sleeping. I searched the kitchen for things to make breakfast with and found pancake mix in the cupboard and a frying pan under the stove. I followed the directions on the bag. I stirred one cup of mix into three-fourths of a cup of water, I lightly greased the pan with butter, I poured slightly less than one-fourth of a cup of batter for each pancake into the pan and cooked them for one and one-fourth minutes, flipping them only once, just as directed. But I managed to burn every one of them. I stood at the counter, looking down at my plateful of pancakes, charred and misshapen, and I let myself daydream that Roger was presently walking up behind me, that he was about to take me by the shoulders, spin me around, and kiss me. But he was still upstairs, asleep.

* * *

If this were a screenplay, I'd write a scene in which Roger and I would arrive at his apartment, after the weekend. We'd sit in the car and he would say something like, "It wasn't too long ago that we were sitting there in that playground. You know?" Then I'd say, "Yeah." Then he'd say, "How does anyone make it work?" "I don't know," I'd say. Then I'd slip the ring off my finger and, stifling a few tears and swiping the hair from my face, I'd say, "Here. Take it." "No," he'd say. "It's yours." Then I would open the door, leave the ring on the seat, and walk away. The pop song that had been playing in the background on the car radio—whiny teenagers covering "Only You"—would crescendo to full volume and float over the fade to black. End credits.

In actuality, there was no fade to black, no music. The shot did not end; it drifted on for another few months, the two of us slowly discovering who we were, or who we thought we were, without the other, without the millions of voices, other people's voices recounting the status quo in our ears, without my mother's voice on a tape recorder and those incessant songbirds singing like they knew the score.

Roger returned to his own voice, to more performances, and to many weekend parties and clubs with his friends, none of these people and places nearly as bad as the ones I'd conjured up in my head. I returned to my college town, to my movies. I cut my hair and made some new friends, made plans to go to my first gay and lesbian film festival in San Francisco the next summer. And one day, while I was walking to class, I called him and said I'd give the ring back the next time I was in Dayton. He said that would be fine.

## Richard N. Bentley

# *Carpathians*

There are countries of the spirit,
Where the villages are lit by torches
And the bears weigh 700 pounds.
The clocks are sad
And strike the wrong hours
While park benches are as empty as the sky.
The tyrannical government
Lies about the weather,
Lies about the sun, moon, stars,
Sex and the mists off the river. The
streets are named Liberation Avenue,
Redemption Boulevard, and Square of
The Sixteenth of January.
This is the world we ran to from the world
While storms of cursing exiles fled the other way
And a father loomed above us all—
Loomed like a mountain range.
A Carpathian father ready to drink the blood of humans.
Seeking counsel I ask,
"Can my father really
Be mastered through
The interpretation of dreams?"
The therapist replies,
"According to Cornell Medical School's
Malaise Inventory, someone who is disturbed
May also have a genuine complaint."
The doctor has a pleasant if inexpressive face
And a disarming manner.
You can see
A fine lucid intelligence in his eyes.
"You must be very confused," the doctor says.
You nod.
"How lonely it must be having your condition.
How baffling and troublesome and unfair."

You bow your head silently in acknowledgment.
Like most educated people,

You are conversant with the basic
Tenets of the therapeutic relationship,
Issues of transference and countertransference
And so forth,
So you do not wish to acknowledge
The fact that you wish with all your heart
To embrace the man, to clamber up
The cliffs of his soaring Carpathian lap,
And remain there
Until you are healed.

Leslie Ringold, photograph

## Erica Lehrer

# *PowerPoint*

Sporting a tailored gray skirt
with knife-edged pleats,
a crisp blue shirt and cufflinks
that glitter like daggers,

I challenged your presentation
in my cutting way. So how
could you imagine that,
more than anything, I wished

you'd disarm me, release me
from my ivory silk bustier,
its intricate hooks and eyes,
its boned bodice trimmed in lace?

## *Dancing with Ataxia*

Is there no poetry
in *cerebellar ataxia* —
words I stumble over
even now
in my spastic-muscled-
balance-challenged-
downbeat-nystagmus-
neurologically-
impaired way?

Tonight,
when you suggested
we dance,
I felt something
like hope,
for haven't we danced
before
in the face of catastrophe?

You'd spin me out
and back
in your embrace.
We'd glide across the floor,
beaming, breathless . . .
forgetting
what worries we had.

These days, I'm leaden
of foot, woozy of head,
as alien to myself
as a Martian.
Neurological signals
not getting through,
I trample your feet, unable
to follow your lead.

When you spin me,
I fly across the room,
out of control, fail to return
to the orbit of your arms . . .
like a planet
forgetting
how to circle the sun.

From the collection of the Editor, photograph

# *Give Me You*

> give orange me give eat orange me eat orange give me eat orange give me give me you
>
> —*Nim Chimpsky*

There is no time, he said, but he had died and no one heard.

A stranger arranged his necktie and fluffed the satin pillow beneath his head while someone else folded his hands across his chest, stiffened so badly he hardly recognized his own fingers.

Across the city, his two sons and their wives are gathering clothes from his bedroom closet, debating which to keep, which to put in a box they've marked for charity. Give the blankets to the Hebrew orphanage in Brooklyn, he wanted to say, they will need it when the Great Depression hits, the one when his own father, Rabbi Meyer, planted a garden at the synagogue to grow the beans and tomatoes on their plates, and he wore his brothers' hand-me-downs until he forgot what proper-fitting pants felt like.

No time.

Even if anyone could hear, what would they know? The turns of their calendar pages, their etched stones arranged to catch the seasons of the moon, their bronze sundials aligned to measure passing shadows? All inventions, he understood now, the foundation of the white-lied lives they live.

His older son is taking his gold pocket watch from the mahogany desk, and he eyes his brother before sliding the smooth roundness into the inner breast pocket of his jacket. For shame, Nathan! I'll give you a whipping for that when you're a boy. No need to turn it into stealing. It's yours. It always was. Didn't your mother teach you better?

Where *is* Hilda? With him or with their boys? Then he knew. In a retirement village, where he once visited her after the divorce, before his body began its quick decline, his lungs filling with fluid that his heart couldn't pump away. Why did he leave Hilda? Maybe he didn't know why, even then. His life was headed elsewhere, that was all.

His younger son, Gabriel, sticks his arm into the sleeve of his best jacket, pulled from his closet. His wife—what is her name?—is urging him to try it on, try it on, see if it fits. What a vintage look. A fabulous style, those wide lapels. Look how it suits you! She claps her hands, then stops herself, ashamed, and takes a different tone. Seymour would be proud if he could see how handsome you look in his favorite jacket.

* * *

Dad did love that old coat, didn't he? It is Nathan, sarcastic as ever, gold watch gleaming from inside his inner pocket. Its tick competes with the pale rhythmic thud of the muscle inside Nathan's chest. Always, the weak heart, that kid. A picture eases into his vision, Nathan with IV tubes twisting across the crisp whiteness of a sheet. Then Nathan, too, understands that there is no time, and the gold watch passes to a new home in the leather box on Gabriel's desk. But Nathan is here now, still caught in time.

His cat, Lottie, sits back on her haunches to sharpen her claws on Nathan's linen suit jacket, slung over the back of a chair in the dining room, as if she knows how quickly he slipped the watch from sight.

Nathan lifts a corner of the wool and sniffs. Good god, it still reeks of smoke. He wore that thing everywhere. Should've buried him in it. Amazing the old man didn't die of mouth cancer, all those damn Cuban cigars. Those boxes of Hoyo de Monterrey he stashed away. Remember?

Dad never got to Cuba. He always dreamed about that. Gabriel takes one of his floral ties from its rack, holds it beneath his chin and studies himself in the mirror. His features are the image of Hilda's, the full pursed lips, the narrow brown eyes and chubby cheeks. The short bow legs. So unlike tall, slender Nathan.

I remember that old flowered tie, says Nathan. It probably stinks, too, and Gabriel puts it away. Remember how we'd choke when he watched the news? The smoke filled the whole house. Mom chewed him out every night and he still wouldn't stop.

You're both lucky you don't have lung cancer. Nathan's wife, her eyebrows pitched knowingly, thin and steep as the stiletto heels on the shoes she's kicked off.

I kind of liked the smell. Gabriel shrugs off the jacket, smells the sleeve of his own shirt. It meant Dad was home. I always knew when he was home from work.

That was the only way we'd know. Nathan laughs. Cigars, and the sound of Edward R. Murrow on the radio.

And those crazy arguments with mom, just when we were going to bed.

Hi Dad, I'd say. Nathan waves his hand as if he's trying to get someone's attention. His knuckles are so hairy. Such smooth boy-hands, but his son waves the blue-veined hand of an old man. What did Dad do? Grunt and raise *The Daily Worker* higher. All that Commie shit, socialist summer camps like Crystal Lake.

The Crystal Lake kid, that's what Mom called me, Gabriel tells his wife. I was conceived there. Summer, nineteen-thirty-nine.

Romantic summer, she says, lifting the cover of his leather cufflink box, embossed with his initials, SNM. Cufflinks, hmm. She picks an onyx pair from the velvet lining. Would you ever wear these?

Not likely. Gabriel laughs and returns to his subject. But Mom and Dad never went back to Crystal Lake again. Two kids ended the romance.

Just a bunch of Commie wannabes at that camp. Nathan again. Not brave enough to join the party, so off they go to socialist summer camp. Should've had little beanie caps on their heads. Labor organizers, folk singers, pseudo-intellectuals, that kind of shit. Dad would've loved to have been important enough for the FBI to knock on our door.

Little ingrates!

* * *

The boys are asleep when the investigators come to the house early on a July morning, the day already promising muggy summer heat. The knock wakes Hilda, and he follows her to the door, sees the brisk flash of their badges. The first man wedges his shoulder and foot past the half-cracked door, and it is too late for Hilda to slam it shut. That gleaming black shoe with its pointed toe. How desperately Hilda shushes him so their boys can dream away undisturbed upstairs, all the while he dodges their questions to save his own life, his job, his home. To save his sons' lives.

The words he spoke later that day! They formed a cage around him for the rest of his life. Not one of his friends saw past the words to the man suffering inside. Didn't they know he would do differently, if only he could do it again? It was like a death. No, it was a death. And you don't get to do death over.

"Who's here?" Gabriel's pajamas are too big for him, hand-me-downs from Nathan, and he tugs at an over-long sleeve. He looks at the men, takes in their shoes, the hats in their hands, the dark ties. "What's going on?"

Hilda rushes to him. Be calm, Hilda. "Dad's going on a business trip."

"Don't you need your suitcase?"

"It's just for the day," he thinks to say. "A meeting. The business took a bad turn."

"You're going into the city?"

"Come kiss Daddy good-bye." Oh for god's sake, Hilda, the boy's twelve years old.

He hugs Gabriel, doesn't stoop for a kiss.

"Oh Dad, hey, if you get by a record store, see if they have 'Crazy, Man, Crazy.' Bill Haley. It's sold out . . ."

Outside, a mourning dove is cooing from its nest on the fire escape, a sound that usually soothes him, even after the worst of quarrels with Hilda. The next-door neighbor, Harry, is out early, pushing his mower across the lawn. A gold star still hangs in his front window to tell the world that his youngest son, only a teenager, died in the war eight years ago. When he sees Seymour with his companions, he turns his back to start another smooth row of freshly cut grass. But not before Harry starts to lift his hand from the mower handle to wave. It is the last time any of his neighbors acknowledges him.

* * *

Important enough, Nathan? What do you know? I should've hit you harder in those boxing lessons I gave you.

Jail. Nathan's wife laughs. Would've been one way to escape your mom for a while. She strokes the fabric of the old jacket, checks the lining for the label.

Italian silk and wool, he could've told her. He bought it at Rosenfeld's for Gabriel's bar mitzvah. Poor Gabriel. At thirteen, he mangles his Hebrew so badly even the Rabbi blushes. And how his voice lurches into soprano, wobbles, then drops again. Through the long endurance, Hilda clutches her program until the paper wrinkles with hand sweat. Never should have forced the kid to go through with this, she whispers.

You're the one who wanted it, he says. Your father would have died if we hadn't, she says, and shushes him. His father sits at the front, dovening even now.

Seymour remembered the cynical passage from Psalms his father loved to intone, "Surely every man walks about like a shadow, surely they busy themselves in vain." He heard it so many times he was determined to make his own life mean something.

Gabriel's wife has closed the cufflink box and slides hangers across the rod in his closet until she eyes a striped Brooks Brothers shirt. Seymour had his good traits.

When he wasn't beating you kids with a leather belt. Nathan's wife.

Right. A brusque laugh from Nathan.

Oh c'mon. We're sitting shiva tomorrow, Nate.

When did you ever get religion? Nathan again. Besides, you were too little to remember the worst.

Hilda always indulged Nathan, her favorite, but their older son was just as surly with her as he was with everyone. Look at Gabriel, how hard he tries to please you, he would remind her. He even has your eyes, your hair and your build. But a mother is always fondest of her first-born, she would say, that's the special child. It's just the order of things, Seymour, the ways things are. But then, Hilda had been the oldest in her own family, so of course she'd say that. Had to support her parents in the Depression, and how often did she remind him of that? You couldn't help being the youngest, she told him, when you were growing up, the baby of the family. Everyone took care of you, and now you're taking care of me. Now I'm the baby. It's the order of things.

Is that why he left her? The order of things?

Gabriel's wife returns the jacket to its hanger, brushes it off. Then Nathan's wife removes it and hands it to Nathan. Here, see how it looks on you, Nate. A good dry-cleaners can get rid of that odor.

Oh Sarah, says Gabriel's wife. But it looks so good on Gabe. Doesn't Nathan already have Seymour's gold watch?

Did Nathan ever blush, even as a child? Could he be blushing?

* * *

But Nathan is a boy now and his father's jacket sleeves hang to the floor when he plays dress-up. A red glow rises from his neck to his cheeks. Delicious cheeks, Hilda calls them and loves to pinch them even if it makes the boy squirm. Now his cheeks look like little apples. Macintosh, Hilda's favorite.

No, not a blush. The cool summer air at Crystal Lake in the Adirondacks reddens Nathan's cheeks, even turns his little knees pink. A cardinal darts about in the trees, a flash of red, its wings stirring the elm leaves. Nothing more beautiful than a bird. But Nathan's shoes are muddy and Hilda bends over his feet, scrubbing desperately at the leather with a rag she's moistened with stream water. The boy is about to cry. What happened?

Little Lord Fauntleroy, Hilda always calls their son, as if to taunt him, Seymour, his athletic father, admired for his prowess at handball, swimming, rowing. What boy dislikes stepping in the mud? What child, girl or boy, refuses to swim in a cool clear stream on a summer day? What boy is afraid of sitting on a pony's back? Oh yes. That eruption of anger he can't control. Rips little Nathan from Hilda's arms and dips his feet into a nice juicy mud puddle, even takes pleasure when his own son cries about his dirty new sandals. Isn't that what fathers are for? To teach their sons courage, adventure? Why the hell does she want Nathan along at an adult camp, anyway? He's the only kid here, always in the way.

Another woman tries to console Nathan, beautiful young Rose whose body he craves, splashing Nathan with cool drops from the stream to change his mood, forget his fretting mother for a while. For god's sake, Hilda, let the boy go.

Could he let Rose go? Her body, lithe, high-breasted, slim-hipped, too good for her pompous husband, a schlemiel named Jake. Too young for that posturing bastard who is willing to trade wives. We're ahead of our times, says Jake, flicking a cigarette ash on the floor, winking at Seymour. Thinks he's so important that the Party couldn't hold a cell meeting without him. Is that what Rose sees in him? Or does she even know?

Beneath the arc of elm trees over the stream, Hilda scrubs at Nathan's muddy sandals, frowning in concentration like her own worried mother might have done back in the Ukraine, back in the old days. The shadows of leaves form a web across her features. Hilda, in love with her own son, what would a few evenings with

Rose matter? He watches the two women with little Nathan, his nervous wife catering to their boy's muddy shoes, Rose laughing, reaching up to catch crystals of water she splashes into the air. Her small breasts rise as she laughs, her teeth white in the sun, her fingers long and slender, filling with the glistening beads that catch the light. She is perfection.

* * *

You are my beau ideal, he tells Rose, as they lie in bed together, and she laughs.

You say that every time. She twists the gold band on his left hand, as if to remind him of Hilda. Or to play with the ring's significance? The curtains cast a shifting shadow across her beautiful skin, a pattern like lace.

No, I mean it.

The evening concert has started up, an oboe's sultry sound, the first rising notes of "Rumanian Fantasy." The cabin's thin green curtains billow in the air as if the musical vibrations have created their own breeze, bringing the smell of the fir trees outside, cool and fresh, so unlike Brooklyn's dense air. Rose buries her face in his neck, folds one leg across his body and he can feel her sweet nest of private hair pressing against his thigh. The trace of musky cologne on her neck mingles with a gentle smell of sweat, more pungent than Hilda's toilet water from Patou, a bottle of Joy, his birthday present to her. My beau ideal, he tells Rose again, but she only smiles in the semi-darkness, and traces her hand along his stomach until he joins with her again.

Where are Hilda and Jake? Hilda reports that they do nothing together but talk during their own private hours. Perhaps she's dancing with Jake, who must surely be awkward, given the way he jerks about on the handball court, flailing his arms, tripping on his own shadow. He's probably boring her with talk of his import business in Queens while he steps on her toes with those flat feet of his.

Beautiful music for dancing, though. He wants to take Rose in his arms, and waltz her across the bare floor of the cabin, naked together. But in his mind's eye he has another glimpse of Hilda, her eyes squeezed tight, as Jake's bare buttocks move like a slow piston above her, the cot beneath them creaking to every sawing motion. What if Hilda has been lying to him? Would she lie to make herself innocent, him more guilty, as a weapon against him when they argue about this summer at Crystal Lake? Hilda is one smart woman.

What's wrong? It is Rose, as he extricates himself from her body. Outside, the band has stopped and in the silence the whine of a lone mosquito makes a jagged path over their heads. Then applause rises from the audience in the small amphitheater down the hill from the cabins, drowns out the invisible insect. He lies quietly, one arm propped behind his head, watching the shadows move across the walls to the rhythmic swing of the curtains. How easy this seems for Rose, each time they are together.

Have you and Jake done this before, switched with another couple like this? Jake told me it's the first time. Is it?

She runs her hand through his chest hair, then reaches lower, but he takes her hand and holds it instead. Never with a woman before, she says. It's amazing.

A woman? What the hell are you talking about?

Hilda. She raises herself on one elbow and studies his face. You don't know?

Deep inside his chest, his breath catches before it can propel the words forming on his tongue. You're lying. Across the ceiling, the shadows graze the exposed wood there, dancing in time to the wind, dancing to nothing.

Oh god. Oh no. She plops her head on the pillow and rests her slender arm across her eyes. She didn't tell you?

You're lying. The curtains blur briefly in their irregular movements in the wind and then his feet hit the floor planks with a bang that shakes the whiskey tumblers on either side of the bed.

I thought you were sophisticated, Seymour. Really. You're acting like a child. Or some capitalist. You think you can own Hilda?

The applause has died and a sole harmonica knifes the air, the tune unrecognizable until a violin joins in and the notes thread together. "Oh Mama I'm So In Love," the Barry Sisters' upbeat song. Hilda knows every word by heart. In Brooklyn, she sings it in the kitchen while he tries to hear the news in the living room. Quickly, he pulls on his pants, buttons his shirt, downs the last of his whiskey before smashing the glass against the wall. Let Rose sweep it up. Or Hilda.

* * *

Hilda is doing a dance with him called the Peabody at their favorite Brooklyn club, Coney Island Nights, a few years before Nathan is born. Together they win the dance contest, but the judges approve mostly of Hilda, the quick movement of her delicate feet to a song by the Barry Sisters. Her blue dress swishes just below her knees, showing off her muscular calves, her slender ankles. The silver buckles of her shoe-straps gleam just above her anklebones, flashing as her feet move on the polished dance floor. A natural touch, she has, nothing anyone ever taught her. Her family is poor as synagogue mice, she jokes, no money for dance lessons. Yet she taught him the Peabody, taught him the quick turns well enough for them to win nearly every contest. She sends the award money to her parents on the Lower East Side, or buys them special challah bread from her favorite Brooklyn bakery just before the Sabbath.

After Nathan is born, they rarely go out dancing any more, but when the boy is old enough, she enrolls him in tap and even ballet lessons before Seymour puts his foot down. The boy's afraid of it, Hilda, can't you see? He doesn't even like the sound of the damn taps. Let me teach him handball, let him learn to swim, how to ride a horse, for god's sake. Stop with the sissy stuff.

But a man should know how to dance. Her eyes harden every time she says that, shining accusations. You knew all the sports, didn't you? Horseback riding, off you rode like a Cossack, whooping your way down Ocean Avenue, leaving me stranded on a horse that barely moved, but maybe that was a blessing. Nibbled grass by the road while I sat there in that saddle terrified of the traffic. Cars ripping past! If you're going to take your wife horseback riding, at least take her to the country.

His failures, always his failures. Sometimes Hilda is the most pig-headed woman he has ever known. You think the foxtrot and waltz are more important than swimming or handball or horses? You're bananas. He jabs his finger at his temple.

Any psychiatrist could tell you that dancing together is a way humans express emotions, share emotions. What? You're so educated and you don't know that?

I didn't say that. If you'd stop talking and listen, you'd know. What I said is you think dancing is more important than swimming or handball. . . oh my god, what the hell are we arguing about, Hilda? This is ridiculous. He hopes she will join his laughter, but she digs in, too deeply entrenched to see the absurdity.

Seymour, why do you think I taught you to dance?

It's like shit, Hilda. The more you stir it, the more it stinks. Just stop with the arguing.

You weren't an easy student, but why do you think I stuck with it?

He already knows this answer, but what is it? He can't remember. Okay, why?

So you would touch me, Seymour. So my own husband would put his arms around me once in a while. I need you to touch me, and not just when you want sex.

Oh now she's starting this old fight. That's the answer, so he'd touch her. What's the next line?

Scientists say people live longer when they're touched. Scientists say, the way her mother quotes the Torah. The same invocation. Hilda is more religious than his own rabbi father had been, she's written her own Torah with mangled quotes from scientists.

Now he remembers the script, the lines he's supposed to deliver. C'mon, be specific, he says. Where's this study been published? Who would let their lives be measured like that? What scientists conducted this research? No respectable scientist, he sometimes adds, but Hilda has already soldiered on with her lines.

Just a hug. Once in a while, put your arms around me. Tears glint in her eyes, threaten to spill. Would you hug me now? Please?

If you ask me, it's not going to be real, is it? Same if you ask me to say I love you, like you're training a damn parrot. You think you can control me? Own me? I have to feel it before . . .

Well, when the hell do you feel it? What does it take? She is yelling through the tears. A trained chimp knows how to express love better than you.

Isn't this a contradiction, Hilda? You're going to yell at me to hug you? Screaming at your husband isn't an effective way to get what you want, if you want to hear me say I love you.

A contradiction? So you want to do one of your Hegelian numbers on me now? Isn't it a contradiction to love someone and not express it?

Develop your own damn critique, he says.

That's just it. You're all about analysis, not feelings.

You think I don't love you, Hilda? Where do you think this house came from? And everything in it? He picks up the red perfume bottle he bought her in Paris, and has an urge to hurl it against the bedroom wall.

But can't you just say it? Don't you ever feel it? Don't you think that's worth more to me than this stuff you buy? Is that what love is to you? Tchotchkes? Instead of giving me things, give me more of your time. She is almost begging, not attractive in a woman who is no longer so young. The lines from her nose to her chin deepen when she talks. Why don't you think about a synthesis instead of spending your time finding contradictions, Seymour?

He returns the red perfume bottle to its proper place, over the small ring that Hilda's perfume has left on her dresser. Synthesis? You don't know what you're talking about, and he leaves, takes a leisurely walk down to the newsstand on the corner for a cigar. Maybe he'll buy her a parrot for their anniversary, but she'd be angry about the cost. You think we're made of money? That's what the bird would learn to say. Made of money? Made of money?

The marriage is a familiar pain, a dull toothache or an itchy rash, the kind of discomfort one searches for almost viscerally, not knowing what to do with oneself in the empty pleasure of its absence. Is it honor or cowardice that keeps him married to Hilda? At times, he feels brave and long-suffering, the kind of man married to a woman in an iron lung or a wheelchair. Tonight, he's a coward, a man who fought in no wars other than those he started himself, with his own friends, his own wife. He's not even brave enough to call a truce, to walk off the battlefield and leave Hilda there alone, wounded and wailing. He imagines her in a wheelchair—an emotional wheelchair—with him behind, pushing, pushing like Sisyphus. Oh, cut it out, you weasel. He clenches his jaw on the new cigar and stops to light it.

She'll be calm when he returns. She is cooking dinner for him and the boys, gedamke chicken, one of her staples. The smell of carrots and onions fills the house. Their bodies turn together in bed, a dance of sleep in which she turns, then he turns, spooning her, his knees tucked behind hers, one arm over her shoulder, and her fingers twine in his own. Synthesis.

* * *

Hilda. She is sitting in her retirement village apartment, a place that combines bed, dining table, and sitting area, much like the space of her parents' Lower East Side tenement. To save money, she has downsized from her former two-room apartment, the place he once visited. Why did he leave her? Not for any lack of love. Time, we invented. But love? Only the scarcity of it was manufactured. But without those two—time and the mad scramble for love—what would life be like for anyone?

Someone is sitting with Hilda and patting her hand, a plump woman he doesn't know. A neighbor? A social worker sent by the management, maybe. On the coffee table sits an enormous fruit basket, apples, oranges and bananas, tied up in cellophane and a white bow with a card tucked in it, the envelope still sealed. Their teenaged grandson, Jason, tears into the plastic and pulls out an orange. All right, Grandma? He asks before ripping off the peel, but she doesn't hear.

Hilda holds a clean tissue, folding and re-folding it. Seymour was brilliant, there was nothing he didn't know, she tells the visitor. We had some good times together. You know, people divorce but you still don't forget the good times. We'd go dancing. Seymour had such strong arms! And you wouldn't believe the tiny waist I had back then. Eighteen inches! Right after we married, what does my husband do? Takes me to Russia, a surprise. Funny kind of honeymoon, no one but Seymour and I could have made a trip like that romantic. That's me, always the romantic. She looks around the room, the cherry bookcase, a porcelain figurine from Japan, a small painting of Venetian canals. Seymour gave me so many beautiful things. Her eyes fall on a red perfume bottle, chipped at the curly edge of the crystal stopper. That's from Paris. Expensive too. See that white rose on it? Hand-painted. I couldn't believe anyone would buy something that special for me. He'd splurge on the craziest things and I'd have to worry like hell about the money.

* * *

In a shop in Montmartre, Seymour picks up a ruby-colored perfume bottle, decorated with a white flower, and admires the careful brush strokes.

"Délicat," warns the shop owner when he gently runs his finger over the raised paint. "C'est très cher. Fait à la main."

The light of late autumn suffuses the shop, its dusty windows muting the last of the evening sun, but the entire room seems lit by glass that has captured old light and sealed it up, incandescent, for hazy days like this one. He holds the red bottle up to the chandelier and it looks as if a fire glows inside the glass. Hilda. He can imagine her face when she unwraps the gift. He would buy her a bottle of Joy by Patou to decant into it. Her favorite.

"Pour ma femme," he tells the shopkeeper. "Elle est. . ." He searches for the word in French. "Triste." Hilda is hardly ever happy anymore.

Perhaps there is more sadness on his face than he knows. The clerk puts his hand on Seymour's elbow, his gaze resting on Seymour's silk tie, as if the sadness is somehow there in the pattern. "Pourquoi?"

So many reasons. Where to begin? Especially in his difficult French. He closes his eyes, surrounded by the sweet heaviness of the air, wondering why he has opened the subject, much less to a foreign stranger. The warmth of the clerk's hand is gentle on his coat sleeve.

Admitting his own foibles does not come easily to Seymour. Even as a young child, he never confesses to wrongdoing, would rather take one of his father's beatings than admit guilt to so much as stealing a cookie. "Can you just say, 'I'm sorry'?" his mother whispers. "Just say the words, Seymour! Your father's gone to get the belt!" But he cannot force his mouth to say the words, much less conjure up the feeling.

In the silence, late afternoon shadows etch the French stranger's face with patterns like the lace on Hilda's favorite satin nightgown. The smell of tobacco on his breath comes sweetly as he speaks sounds Seymour does not understand. Yet the look on his face gives the words meaning, and he gestures to two overstuffed chairs behind the counter. "Asseyez-vous," and pulls the chairs closer together.

When he sinks down into the upholstery, he realizes he is more fatigued than he knew. How many miles has he walked today, spurred by tomorrow's departure date? Down the wide corridors of the Louvre, through flea market alleyways filled with Asian textiles, then down into the Metro's maze, lugging his last-minute sacks of fabrics. On the descent, the underground air rushed to his nostrils like the breath of a strange animal, a sour odor of urine and stale perfume. Loud smells, rivaling the roar of the trains for attention. He would miss those strange smells, even the musty odor in his room at Hotel Bizet in the Pigalle, where a few jazz clubs still kept a rhythm of pre-war Paris.

No wonder he was exhausted. And now climbing the steep hills of Montmartre for a last gift for Hilda until rain forced him to seek the shelter of this store's awning over its window filled with glass delicacies. Fragile and beautiful like Hilda.

A bell tinkles at the door as the clerk makes a final jerk on the knob before locking the shop. "Fermé. C'est tard," he shrugs and removes a whiskey decanter from a cabinet, places the bottle and two delicate glasses on a tray. Just so, his slender hands as careful with the items as a Japanese woman arranging a tea ceremony, as if he has been waiting for Seymour.

The whiskey slides smoothly down Seymour's throat, twice. Outside, two young women, arm in arm beneath an umbrella, peer into the window, point to a vase on display. The light inside is too dim for them to see further, and Seymour feels sheltered by that knowledge, as secluded as if he were camping on a cool late summer weekend in the Adirondacks with Hilda. Nothing to disturb them. And has he ever drunk whiskey so mellow? Ah, it soothes the throbbing in his feet.

Across from him, on a small wood table made for playing cards, the Frenchman shakes loose tobacco into a cigarette paper, expertise in his fingers, massaging the paper into a roll with his fingertips. The ritual is a meditation for him, Seymour can see that, and he glances from the man's hands to his face, his hair loose over his forehead, darkly curling at the ears. An American man would have gotten a haircut or slicked it back with pomade. He extends the finished cigarette to Seymour, the lit end illuminating the deep creases in his palm. As he offers the tobacco, the man gazes out at the rain. There is no question that Seymour will accept the offering. It is scripted somehow, like the tattoo peeking from beneath the rolled cuff of his sleeve. *Numbers*? Yes, numbers, my god, and Seymour resists an urge to stroke the inked skin.

"Votre femme?" The words circle on a smoke ring and dissolve slowly.

Yes, his unhappy wife who started this silent conversation in the back of the store. Where is Hilda now? It is still late morning in Brooklyn. She is wheeling a grocery cart through Waldbaum's, a duck tied up in white butcher paper, Seymour could see that now, now that his vision is no longer limited by the body in the casket.

But Hilda never cooks duck. Never experiments beyond her few recipes. What kind of life did she have while he was away?

Outside, the strains of a jazz band start up from a club called Chez Bricktop across the street. The music of Sidney Bechet, a famous Negro saxophonist from New Orleans, slides through the darkening light, clear and smooth as tears. Or as this whiskey. He takes a deep sip, stretches out his legs and rests his head against the back of the chair, the riffs meandering into his memories. He closes his eyes, inhales the cigarette in the darkness behind his eyelids. Now "The Quincy Street Stomp," Bechet's lively number about Brooklyn, explodes Seymour's pleasantly melancholic mood. Oh, this is the life! Bechet's sax, a good whiskey, and a night in Paris. Even if he *is* alone.

How long has the warmth pressed against his knee? It moves in circles now, smoothing the tweed of his pants, massaging the muscle of his thigh. He opens his eyes at a gentle squeeze. The stranger is ready to pour, his eyes pointing at the empty glass Seymour holds. The face is still patterned, an imprint from the leaves on a small plant in the window, a veil of shadows across the features. Seymour nods, puts the now-full glass to his lips.

Then the words come, a confession fragmented by the French he has yet to master. The lake in the Adirondacks at the end of summer. 1939. And Rose. Was it really his fault? Swim, what is the word for swim? He didn't know Jake couldn't swim. Or barely row a boat, for that matter. He had to start up the propeller to get to shore. Why did he invite Jake out? He didn't want his company, he remembers that. So full of himself, that man, thought he was so clever with his constant jokes, his labor stories—how many times did Jake brag that he'd nearly been killed by hired thugs? Nine lives, like a stray cat at the doorstep. Why did he invite Jake out on the lake that day, with clouds gathering and a wind puckering the water's surface?

"Il est mort?" The clerk's voice comes dusky, gentle, and the words are smoother than they sound in English.

Seymour shakes his head. No, no. Just an accident. *But I wanted him dead,* he thinks.

The jazz club across the street offers up a new tune now, a lively piano piece, carrying him to the screened porch of the mountain cabin when he told Rose about the accident. Jake in the hospital, his leg sliced open by the boat propeller. He'd thought surely it was almost severed when he pulled him into the boat. Blood everywhere, Jake clutching at his thigh, the boat slapping the water in the rush to shore, to the horrified faces who heard Jake's screams. Someone had already run to call an ambulance when he docked the boat, another was already pulling his belt loose, to tourniquet the leg, and a woman held Jake's hand, wiped his forehead with a handkerchief. He ran to Rose's cabin to tell her Jake's leg looked nearly severed. *Or to claim her?*

So young and intelligent, that Rose, to be married to such a fool. Rose was wearing her blue flowered sundress, the neckline skimming the top of her breasts, showing a small beauty mark there. She pulled the skirt up to her face when she heard the news, sagged against the porch railing. Those long, slender legs and bare feet, browned by the sun, exposed as she lifted her dress like a little girl might. Hilda. Where did she come from? She grabbed Rose's hand and off they ran to the dock. He picked up Rose's sandals from the porch and followed them. She could cut her feet on the sharp pebbles in the sand.

She was too distracted to put on the sandals until after they were sitting in the emergency room at the hospital in nearby Garrattsville, pale with shock that Jake might lose his leg. Hilda held Rose's hand, her lips moving silently, her eyes closed. A prayer? My god, he'd never known Hilda to pray. A secret belief, or a desperate reach for magic? The nurse was smiling when she emerged through the swinging doors. Jake's wound wasn't even deep, the doctor had stitched and bandaged it and Rose could go back to see her husband now. He and Hilda could go back, too, she said. First he needed to finish his cigarette, maybe light another. *All that screaming and blood for a little nick on the leg! My god.*

A fresh cigarette brushes the Frenchman's lips, a match flaring up to light the tobacco. Before the man waves out the flame, it illuminates his face and for the only time, his eyes meet Seymour's, draw closer.

When they rise at last, the Frenchman steadies himself against the counter, rocking it, and the tinkle of breaking glass follows. When he holds Hilda's perfume bottle to the square of gray light at the window, a chip in the frilled edge is visible. He turns it, and turns it again, as if a different angle will eliminate the new flaw.

"Désolé," he tells Seymour. They both stare at the glass with its perfect gesture of imperfection, and then he reaches under the counter for tissue paper to wrap it, as if he holds an infant. His fingers smooth and tuck the folds of tissue, another slow ritual, confident and careful as his arrangement of the whiskey decanter and glasses, and the tender rolling of their cigarettes. The package is beautiful when he hands it to Seymour, a present tied with soft blue ribbon, tucked into a box lined with satin. "Un cadeau pour vous." He turns away, as if giving some delicate part of himself, a seed of remorse, perhaps. Or is there a sliver of delight in his smile, leaving his mark on Hilda's red decanter?

Laughter erupts from the sidewalk outside and the sound of a solitary saxophone floats out into the night. People are leaving the jazz club, lifting bright umbrellas, a merry toast to the rain.

* * *

What were you so worried about, Mrs. Meyer? Hilda's visitor frowns in faux concern. It's all right to accept gifts from your husband.

Of course Hilda worried, he says, what the hell do you know? The visitor does not hear him, but he continues. Why wouldn't a woman like Hilda worry about money? For god's sake, her family had it even worse than mine did. Who the hell is this idiot woman, Hilda? Why did you invite her here?

Of course I worried about money, Hilda says. I still do. If my savings run out, I'll be out on the streets. Living in some Medicaid facility. Rich people never have to worry about that. If Seymour had been more sensible . . .

Rich people. Always with the rich people. No matter how much he earned, it wasn't enough to ease her fears, how to make more, how to spend less, whether to save it. Under socialism, money wouldn't rule their lives, wouldn't dictate who people are, how they measure themselves. Money drives them apart, drives Hilda crazy. Or is it something else, something more?

Being married to Hilda is enough to make any man lose his senses. He can barely talk anymore, she interrupts him every time he opens his mouth. Sometimes she even argues against Russia, against Marxism, against everything he stands for, every principle he loves. Your socialism is all about abstract people, she tells him, but when people are real, do you care about them? You know how to think, Seymour—here she jabs her index finger to her temple—but you don't know how to feel.

Tell me, Hilda. If I didn't care about people, could I accept Gabriel? His voice is a low hiss so the boys upstairs can't hear. Isn't that important, caring about people, regardless of who they are? Or who they belong to?

Hilda's face whitens and she sinks into a kitchen chair. You don't know.

Yes, that's just it. We don't know, do we? How can you tell me that I don't know how to feel?

She rises to put an old record album, *Ballad For Americans*, on the turntable, and Paul Robeson's voice becomes a thick veil of sound between them. Hilda feels for Paul Robeson, all right. She sets the needle on "Drink to Me Only With Thine Eyes" as if she's in love not only with voice but also with the face on the album cover, those intense eyes and sensuous lips.

He knows one thing for sure: Hilda loves Nathan more than anyone in the world.

But there is a second sure thing he knows: the way time links one word, then one sentence, to the next, and the way both time and words distort love. Whatever that is, love.

* * *

Jason has finished the orange, and stacks the scoops of rind in the palm of his hand. Ready to go, Grandma?

Where?

The boy glances at the floor. Funeral home. He looks at her again, hesitates before he speaks. Grandpa.

You're driving? Why the hell did your father send you? Can't he be a mensch, for once? Where are Gabriel and Nathan?

Our two sons are claiming my belongings, he could tell Hilda if she could hear him. And Jason, have patience with your grandmother.

* * *

What'll we do with that cat? Gabriel eyes Lottie, a Siamese rubbing herself against his ankles. I'm allergic and Mom can't possibly take her in the retirement village. Not that she'd want to anyway.

One helluva sweet kitty. Nathan scoops her up and hands the cat to his wife, Sarah. Siamese are the most intelligent. Sarah strokes her beneath her chin and Lottie's black ears jerk, a signal, if only Sarah knows how to read it. Lottie wants down, enough of the petting. The cat knows. She is wiser than any of them. Give me Lottie, Seymour says. Give her to me. He tries again, but he cannot project a sound. The effort is too great, he is losing words. Words belong to time, and there is no time.

Lottie stretches, then flows in a single movement from Sarah's arms onto the faded Persian rug in his bedroom. She leaps into the cardboard charity box and curls up on a bundle of his shirts, her gray tail wrapped around her haunches, the tip twitching.

Looks like the old man was spying on his neighbors, some naked woman. Nathan stoops to peer through the finding scope standing at his bedroom window, trained on a birdfeeder in the back garden. A golden finch is sitting there, framed in the scope's circle like a brilliant photograph. Maybe Nathan can see it before it flies away. He hunches there, eye to the scope—don't adjust it! It's set perfectly—and watches the solitary bird, the sun gleaming on its yellow feathers. Nothing more beautiful than a bird, he has told both his boys, but they are never interested. Nathan clasps his slender hands behind his back, suddenly as still as the finch.

Sarah taps Nathan on the shoulder, holding out the old silk and wool jacket. At least try it. It's Italian. Beautiful fabric. We can have it cleaned and ready in no time.

Nathan covers his eyes with his hand and turns away, then leaves the room.

Nate? Gabriel starts to follow, but turns back when sobs erupt from the hallway, muffled by the closing of the bathroom door. Let him be. He's all right, he tells Sarah.

Lottie watches with her cool blue eyes, shifting first to Gabriel, then to him, her eyes flicking like a metronome waiting for the music until her eyes fix on him. He feels the pull of the long black pupil in the center, a door opening there.

Hilda is smoothing her finger over the raised brush strokes on her perfume bottle from Paris, observing for the first time its intricate beauty. She turns it slowly until the chip catches an exhilarating glint of sun.

Give me you, Hilda. Give me you. The words are his, but no one can hear. He sees them—his sons, Hilda, all of them—in their prison of orderly words and time.

Get me out.

He turns and escapes into the promise of Lottie's eyes.

# *The Cherry Tree*

Like some zen bee garden
they were drawn to it
plunging in and out of
those used pink blossoms.

Each drink of nectar
their own private
christening, a divine dance
in some imagined paradise.

I watched them for hours
working, the tireless devotion
of it. The way they made
an ecstatic fuss, their black bodies

consumed by the vibratory hum
their yellow stripes afire.
How did they become so singular
desiring only the flower

and nothing else?
When all those practiced petals fell
the bees disappeared. I stood witness.
Felt the flat air. Reckoned too
with oblivion.

# *Looking Up From Bleak Headlines at These Friable Trees*

and earth parched beneath an overburdened sky
sky like a mother with five children
and no money coming in

All day I've been building a chassis for thought
but the innards are at the shop for repair
touch the keys and there's no give, no give—

(*chassé chassé* so bleak the day) no give
with this word-salad mind, its slivers
of dreams and bad news

its hunger and heady belief
that sky is its hand mirror
handmaiden, mother

And so when sky pulls close her stony coat
fragments spill from holes in her pockets
raining down on me like meteors

# *The Sum of Its Parts*

He says he's felt
time snag like silk
through his hands

the night that lurched
from a mountain road
and crashed over them

the time her name
slipped from his tongue
a name he'd have
carved into cliffs

She reminds him
of each day that
lingered lighthearted

afternoons handed
back and forth
like a bubble

Each hour that spilled
like a weasel
into its burrow

delicate head
long white hide
black-tipped tail

## *Morning Nature Walk*

It's hard to be human,
to know more than we should,
memories bright as dead pine needles
that scrub niches for shoes.
Pebbles grind under the weight of what worries.
The breeze, where is it coming from?
The sun diagnoses today's weather.
Fire probability: HIGH
When you died, I lay on the front lawn un-
controllably.
On the ground there is no shelter,
no signs telling you which way to go,
where to turn. There are stops everywhere.
My hope, I guess, the roots would hear.
But there was nothing I was able to.
Aerosol scours the waste cans,
old movies drift off the TV.
Kaposi sounds like the name of a flower.
Who knew it was poisonous.
Your eyes pop open like suitcases when the nurse
comes to switch out your pillow.
Sometimes I hear whole families cry like seabirds.
*Go long,* the coach said. *Go long. Deep.*
You were always better at that than I was,
but because I came first, womb-drenched,
one minute before, you never believed me.
How long do you contain grief's desire?
After a while, a photograph becomes
a kind of mirror on the dresser.
I keep wanting to turn it around.
Unfolding myself next to you,
I lie wearing one of your old shirts.
Outside, a lawn mower chips away at the grass.
Who said it was too high?
And why does the gardener confuse it with cutting?
The sprinkler system turns itself on and won't shut up.
It's not so bad when you know what comes afterward, but

where did all dandelions disappear to?
I sort of counted on them.
*Watch your step.*
*This is where the grass starts to get slippery.*
*Now look at the Mule Ear turn its back.*
*See the way the petals split,* the guide says, *divide.*

From the collection of the Editor, photograph

# *Cruelty to Animals*

She drowns once a week. In a tight neon pink swimsuit and baby blue goggles, she hops to the water along the scalding rocks that pass for sand on our inch of the Gualala River. At the edge she performs quick and useless stretches, probably because someone once told her she should stretch before swimming. Reaper's on lifeguard duty so he's up in the God-chair, stoned, slick with tanning oil, not the sunblock we make the kids wear. The rest of the counselors and I watch from shore. Usually we spend our free time taking long showers, sneaking rolled cigarettes, and thinking up cruel nicknames for each other, but this is Wednesday, the middle of the week, the day Chantal likes to drown.

I don't know why I'm thinking about her. Maybe it's because nobody calls me anymore. My telephone's so damn quiet. Lounging there amid a tangle of cords and chargers, it's become introspective. My phone knows why nobody calls.

She splashes the river up her body until her belly's wet, then sinks slowly, yelping when water covers her chest. It's hot and breezeless. I want to be wet and cold. I want to immerse my own boobs in water. Maybe I'll swim instead of shower. I sniff. The air smells like crap. Sometimes it's dead animals, but usually it's just Reggae Time, the hippie music festival up river that makes the whole valley stink of Port-O-Lets and weed and armpits. Reaper, whose name is Nathan, wants me to go there with him for our day off but I'm not sure.

There's a terrifying dog on a chain across the street. It's a Doberman.

I still hate all the animals of the forest: squirrels and raccoons and possums and mice. I still hate the bugs too: ticks and flies and wasps. The animals got trapped under the lodge and we had to wait for them to die. The bugs got trapped inside the lodge and we had to swat them away from our burgers.

Chantal readjusts her goggles, then goes under to search for minnows with the other loser kids. The cool girls have already swum across the river to the cliffs opposite the camp to watch boys jump. The cool girls wear bikinis and swim and run so gracefully it's hard to catch them in the blinding sunlight. The losers rise to the surface like bits of plastic on water. Then they drift off with the current, or, on our inch of river, where the water's stagnant come August, they float, waiting for the water ticks to land on them. There they are—the fat and the skinny, the too tall and the too short with their water wings and inner tubes.

Damn, I say to nobody in particular.

Tragic, Monkey says, a moment later. Her name's Marie, but we call her Monkey because she's tiny and can do flips and has a whisper of a moustache.

Like they make you sick with their needing you so much, I say and I mean it. I feel sick. Maybe it's the sun. The sun at Camp Outdoor Adventure is a pain in the ass. It's unrelenting and white.

It's funny that I don't remember the normal kids. Their faces, freckled and smirking and running past, are a blur. It's the kids like Chantal I think about while I cook eggs or heat soup or light up a grill. I love to light up a grill. The smoky smell reminds me of the campfire at night and the way the smoke clung to my hair, even after I'd wash it.

The second time Chantal drowned Director Doc called her mother, who said: She does stuff like this all the time. She'll quit eventually. Look, I gotta go, I'm at work.

I tried to imagine Chantal's parents: dad wears plaid and mom works two part-time jobs. Then I tried to imagine these people naming their child *Chantal*.

Plugging her nose, she goes down. Back up she gasps for air. My question is this: When she woke up that day did she know she was going to pretend to drown again?

I haven't seen Monkey since the accident. I haven't seen anybody since the accident.

It takes a while for her to get warmed up. A few of the counselors get bored and go back up to camp along the rough planks we'd placed over the rocks. With every step the boards plunk and echo in our small valley. It's probably a safety hazard. Camp Outdoor Adventure is a cheap camp. Set along the slope of a scraggly yellow hill that runs down to the river, it's a camp in decline.

Maybe it'll work, Monkey says. This time.

Maybe not, I say.

I know Chantal. She's in my cabin, Cabin 10. I always have Cabin 10, the oldest girl cabin, because, as Director Doc says, I'm tall and "mature." I'm only nineteen. He just says that cause I have big boobs.

I'm Petra but they call me Pete. I got the nickname two years ago because I slept with Truck, the staff nurse, but wouldn't be his girlfriend, so he called me a lesbian and that translated to Pete. He said I had lesbian hair, which I didn't, but it didn't even matter cause I grew it out anyway, into this long black braid I carry behind me.

Why do I always go back to Chantal? Her skin was the dull color of dust and it matched her hair. She was immature but she was only thirteen. She wasn't the only one who hadn't kissed a boy, so why was she the only one punished? The other inexperienced girls were taken under the ugly, freckled wings of the girls with experience. They pranced the ugly hillside picking out frightened boys to mutilate with their sticky lips. Those girls were survivors. They were like animals out in the woods abandoned by mothers but instead of curling into a fetal ball and shaking to death, these girls thrived. Arms locked to each other like jewelry clasps, they roamed in packs and terrorized the weak.

Chantal's a lifer—a camper sent here for the whole summer. It's the worst kind of punishment. She arrived on the first day of camp in fake diamond-studded sunglasses, her lips shining with bubble gum lipgloss and I thought: divorce. Using gestures learned from television, she told the rest of the girls about her mom's fancy car and about how her daddy had a plane and was going to teach her how to be a pilot. Two days later, Latiqua, a tiny twelve-year-old with braids to her waist, wore Chantal's sunglasses to breakfast and the rest of the girls in Cabin 10 stole her tube of lipgloss and smeared it all over a boy with a face like a stunned possum.

After three weeks of camp, she stopped telling other kids about those cars and planes. She was quiet, probably hoping she'd blend in. But that didn't work either. They wrote "Bitch" on her camp t-shirt after only knowing her an hour. Kids could really sniff her out.

The needy kids wanted to hold my hand. They wanted to give me a hug. They wanted to fax their moms at the office. They wanted to hang on me, touch me—force me—to like them.

I like siesta-time best, Chantal said and I knew why. Those girls couldn't be horrible when I was there. Siesta came after lunch. It was a forced hour of relaxation in the cabin. The girls whispered, hissing about boys and makeup and lanyards and music while Chantal brushed my hair. She always wanted to brush my hair and I couldn't say no. Or, I said yes just to prove to the other girls that her touch wasn't toxic.

Starting at the roots, she worked her brush through my tangles, taking her time because when she was done there was nothing else to do but lie in her bunk and pretend to sleep because the snakes wouldn't speak to her.

Should I have been around more? Maybe. But there was Nathan and the walk-in fridge when it was hot. There was Monkey and the place out behind the staff showers where I went to read and smoke joints. And I was afraid. Her touch was toxic. Needy kids, weak kids—they were like an infectious disease. They were catching. You had to jump out of the way or their neediness would rub off on you and then you were screwed, back to square one, the bottom of the pack.

It's been proven to be a load of shit that animals smell fear. They simply pick up body language. Dogs and horses and lions and tigers sense bulging eyes, skittish movements, and quaking knees, but I think that humans do smell fear, or at least weakness. I'm not a scientist, but I'm sure they do. For example, half the time if I see people eating alone at restaurants my heart breaks with their loneliness. The other half the time I'm envious. There they are with a book and a glass of wine and a bowl of pasta and they don't have to listen to anybody else's problems. But here's the thing—I can tell in a split second which half to envy and which to pity. Pity. Who am I to pity someone else? Well, I like to be alone for one thing; loneliness has never touched me. But I've never spent so much time alone as I have this past year. It was a car accident. Four dead. I survived.

Here's what would happen: Chantal would take her time wading out towards the deep end of the river, the far side near the cliffs. Then she'd disappear for a minute, only to pop up towards the cliffs. She'd look around. Moments later we'd hear a small cry, like a faraway hawk, then she'd thrash in the water, go slack on her belly, and drift.

Man down. That's what Tattoo, the bearded cook from Germany, would say.

Showtime, Reaper would say. He'd leap from the lifeguard's chair, stare out towards Chantal's lifeless body in the water and, shielding the sun from his eyes, blow his whistle three times. The whistles would multiply infinitely in our valley.

Perplexed, kids would look up. A boy—mid-jump from the cliffs—would contort his body into a question mark before he splashed into the water. Sly little girls would glance left and right, wondering whom they should help.

Girls always wanted to appear to be the ones to help.

Tonight Monkey's going to wheel me to the movies and then we can go get beers at Ricky's Bar. When she sees me she'll have to laugh because if she cries I'm going to be pissed.

For a few hours after being rescued Chantal would be happy. Pampered, coddled, and cuddled, she'd sit in the camp lounge, smothered in blankets, and bask in the attention of the other girls. Boys too. They'd bring her lanyards or friendship bracelets they'd made for their sisters or mothers. Chantal would accept all of it. She would be the most kind to those who had been the most mean.

The news would come during dinner and it would catch like fire among the campers. I was always shocked it was the other lifers, hurting one of their own, who'd tell on Chantal.

She did it last week.

She'll do it again.

Then the kindness and the coddling would disappear as if kindness and coddling were real, tactile items that could be handed out like objects then snatched away.

What in a child's life is premeditated? Did I plan to terrorize Ashley? Did Chantal wake up knowing she was going to drown that day? I'm thinking back to my own childhood. I calculated what time Mom would come back from the grocery store to make sure that I'd washed and put away my ice cream dish. But I didn't have any long-term plans. It wasn't possible. Children are like animals. They see the next hour, not the next day or week or year or decade or millennium. The moment about to happen is the horizon. The moment previous was the worst moment of their lives. I'm twenty-three now. I see the future and it's a straight, flat road in a valley between two lavender mountains. It's forever and it never bends or curves. My arms have become strong and tough; my legs are worthless. Nobody's kissed me since the accident or begged me with his gray eyes to go to Reggae Time with him. I live on a first-floor apartment in downtown San Jose, three miles from Mom's house. I'm finishing college. There are scholarships for people like me so I don't have to work—so I have a lot of time to think about my silent telephone.

The accident happened on Steinbeck Drive. We swerved and hit an oncoming truck. I was in the backseat. The last thing I remember is fighting over which radio station to play.

Chantal's dark wooden hairbrush had been her grandmother's. On the flat side was a carved daisy. Daisies are my favorite, she said one day in her raspy, urgent voice. Even though they stink.

Wherever she is, Chantal is eighteen now. She's an adult. I wonder if she'd be afraid of me. Maybe she'd think paralysis is catching. Or maybe she'd realize how close she came to it and she'd have pity, which would be worse. Pity cripples. I think about all the people I've crippled with my pity. And deep inside I feel like I deserve what I got. I feel like everybody deserves to be crippled and weak and pitied. Just to know what that feels like.

In the blue mornings at Camp O.A. we raised the flag and sang that horrible song, "Everything is Beautiful." Fog from the coast, only ten miles away, dampened the patchy yellow grass. The kids looked particularly vulnerable in morning shadows. Even the snakes, the ones who hissed Bitch and Ugly, sang like stone angels in the soft blue light. They sang the way believers sing. Chantal opened her mouth so wide when she sang, as though the louder she sang the happier she might become. Sometimes I was overcome with how grotesque everything was—the kids and the stupid camp and Reaper and the food and the way we sang cheap songs about God with Tattoo accompanying on acoustic guitar.

I go back to Chantal because I was supposed to protect her even though I was only nineteen. But that's no excuse. Aren't we who we are all the time? Ashley was a pudgy ice-blonde girl. We were four years old together. In the mornings our mothers dropped us off at a farm on the outskirts of town and we spent the day there while they, our mothers, went to work. Ashley always cried when her mother left so I comforted her by putting my arms around her. When she stopped crying, though, I missed her tears so much I pinched her arms and legs with my fingernails until she started to cry all over again. Then I put my arms around her to comfort her.

And so on and so forth all day long.
Why did I do that?
Better question: Why did she allow that?

A girl tugged on my arm in the middle of the night.

Someone peed, she complained. She held her nose. I can smell it, she said.

Oh God, I thought, let it not be—

It was.

Why did it have to be Chantal?

When I was a little older, the rest of the kids and I in daycare ran around that farm in packs. But there was danger—a German Shepherd named Ralph who liked to hump. If you ran too fast and got ahead of the pack, Ralph would hump your leg. If you were too slow, Ralph would hang back and hump your leg. This meant that for years I perfected the art of running directly in the middle of the pack for fear of getting humped.

Reaper drags Chantal out of the water. Kids squat on the beach, whispering amongst each other. The rest of the counselors and I sprint to Reaper and stand around Chantal. It's remarkable the way she keeps it up: her body moves under his arms like a dummy made of sand, her eyelids flutter but never open. We take our roles seriously as well. Monkey grasps my hand. Reaper cradles Chantal's head under her arm and whispers Chantal, Chantal. It's sweet the way he says her name and gives her the chance to go through all of the complicated maneuvers required in her recovery.

We wait for her maneuvers but they don't come. Chantal is blue-cold even though the sun is so white and hot. The kids are still as stones on the beach. Reaper searches our faces.

Do it, I say. What the hell are you waiting for?

He tilts her neck back and breathes air into her lungs.

Reaper tilts her head and breathes air into her lungs again.

The dog on the chain will not let up. Every time someone walks by the damn thing just barks louder.

Monkey's late. The movie starts at seven and it's already six-thirty. It's not like we can just run over to the theater ten minutes before. It takes a while for me to go somewhere. I'm pretty slow. It's actually funny. I'm at the bottom of the pack now but I'm definitely not getting humped.

One day Chantal didn't show up for lunch. It was a Thursday, the day after she drowned the first time. Tattoo had made chili with cheese and onions.

I found her on the beach, jumping on the planks over the rocks.

What are you doing?

Her t-shirt was damp with sweat. She jumped again, landing with her knees straight so that the impact would be strong.

Stop it, Chantal. That's weird.

She jumped one more time, then leaned over and picked up the plank. Ha, she said. There were two mice smooshed and bloodied in the sharp crevices between the plank and the rocks. Chantal was excited. She showed me where the mice lived and how, if she rustled her feet in the dirt and grass near their hole, a whole bunch of them would run out and then she could kill them by jumping on the planks.

My telephone receives a call. It's Monkey, or Marie, as she calls herself, informing my telephone that she is held up at her job at the Gap and will not be able to come over like we've been planning all these months. It's okay, I tell Monkey. Don't worry about it. I understand.

I don't need somebody feeling sorry for me. Better to be left alone. I'm going to light up the grill on my small back porch and cook up a steak. I want that smoky smell in my hair.

Reaper tilts her head and breathes air into her lungs again. Silence settles in our valley and, below that silence, there's a groovy bassline from a band playing at Reggae Time. River water forms drops on Chantal's skin but they quickly disappear with the heat from the sun.

Now, years later, I imagine what went on in Chantal's head when she was floating face down in the water.

1. Her eyes are open in her goggles. She's alert. Are they coming? Do they care? She feels ripples in the water. She senses a boy's splash nearby. Something's coming towards her. Reaper. She senses him before she can feel the water move around her body. She's holding her breath. She spasms her body for fun, as though that is what would happen, medically speaking,

before a drowning. There he is. Someone's coming for her. She can't wait till after, for the skinny-armed hugs and the squirrel smiles.

2. Her eyes are closed. She's actually drowning. She's not going to die, but she hopes she'll lose consciousness. They'll have to put her in one of the rough wooden beds in the nurse station. She'll stay there and live there, unconscious, but secretly conscious, for the rest of the summer. They'll transport her home in the rough wooden bed. They'll tie it to a pickup truck and cart her home and she'll stay in those white sheets for the rest of her life.

3. Her eyes are open inside the goggles. She loves the bottom of the river. She's so still the fish aren't afraid. They are ugly little fish, the dullest browns and blues and oranges she's ever seen. The rocks shine gold where streaks of sun hit them. She thinks: the rocks are real. The fish are real. Every inch of her skin is comforted by soft river water, like a magic blanket of water. She thinks: remember this!

Reaper tilts her head and breathes air into her lungs again. Her mouth opens, spilling a glassful of water. She becomes less and less blue, until she's dust-colored again.

Nothing to see here, Monkey shouts at the campers on the beach. Go back to your cabins and change for soccer.

Chantal opens her fat green eyes. I drowned, she whispers. Her voice is calm and dreamy. I want to hit her.

## M. Michael Hanner

# *Christmas Eve*

We are the last dancers today when the hall closes at four.
The market almost drowns out our Firpo *milongas,*
We laugh at our gliding over stumbles of my sloppy lead.
Today our dance is pivots and *trespies.*
We hold our flame against the face of winter's geometry.

She used to take the train north
and stay in the Mallory Hotel in Portland.
She would eat a secluded dinner in the dining room.
Paired white columns with gold painted capitols
below a thick white cornice, chandeliers and indirect lighting.
If she could have come again this year
she'd have had Yorkshire pudding with the roast beef
because it's Christmas. The dining room is a quarter full.
The same quiet people. Waiters in black and white;
at each place, little paper cups
filled with candied almonds in white and pink.

Later tonight, there will be church—
another tangible dock to visit, dazzled and amused
like a tour of a marshland as we become exotic birds,
we wade in the shallows, boasting of our crocodiles.
We will hold candles and hug strangers.

After church, a fire of fir and madrone,
we open the presents that have lain
beside the black Japanese chest in the living room.

And with the bill, a last paper cup arrives
this time with salted walnuts which sometimes
she eats and sometimes she saves for later.

## *Old Boxes*

My brother is in the house of the Lord,
or so my mother would say. We never
talked about the death, but she was fond
of saying, *Willie would be 28 today if he had lived.*

At the time I didn't know what to say to that.
Still don't—I used to think there was something
wrong with me not to feel more for this unmet child,
my senior silent partner. Today, sitting in my small

cardboard city of boxes, finding his death certificate—
he would be 72. Some stranger, some bit of lamplight,
I feel tattered, no messages on the answering machine.
The last of the dogwood leaves should fall today.

## Erinn Batykefer

# *The First of the Year*

Imagine the tight bud of a calendula unwinding
white as leaves, white as dirt and sun.

The beginning is always planeless, imbricate:
sky fused to branch, to powerline;

the creek no longer creek but a depression
of colder, slicker white.

There are no flowers here. Before we spoke,
we touched.

World as whole cloth. Each emptiness
a texture.

Begin again snowblind, benighted
by light. Be unburdened and gaining speed;

move into the unshadowed world as if through
darkness, hands first—

soon enough, sunlight will fracture through
the valley, edged and ruinous.

Behind it, the sky is already a shattering blue
we will break against.

# *Not Jane-Who-Waits*

1.
Shall I call you Prometheus?

You showed me fire when you should not, lit me
wicklike, and molded the maiden clay of governess
into Jane-who-burns.

Were you surprised when she fired, irrevocably,
to stone? All winter, my footsteps crackled
through the cold hall like premonition.

Like transgression.

2.
I will not be Jane-who-waits
for fate or fortune, but Jane-who-climbs
the highest hill in the county,

who peers toward the far off and coming;

as-the-crow-flies-Jane, who does not walk
the winding trail through forest, ferns, but burns
clean through,

and rises, smokelike,

to see the relentless trajectory:
in every direction, the same horizon—story's end
a promontory of rocks we must be flung from.

3.
To think—had I but let her first fire lick your flesh,
you might be punished sufficiently already,

scarified and mine.

But I emptied the ewer onto your sleep, wishing only
to save you from a pyre of bedclothes—

I knew nothing of parity then.

4.
Let me winch our future forward, gouge the sight
from your head, leave one eye hanging
like a bare bulb, by a nerve.

Is it not crippling, this heat?

Come close, and I will show you what I have endured,
scuttle raptor-sharp fingers over your chest
and sink them down to liver.

Let me even us.

Come close and let me lame you—
you need me and I need you
broken.

Kathryn Alvarado, photograph

## Beth Alvarado

# *Notes from Prague*

It has always seemed to me that it takes time for memories to settle. Sometimes you form them into a story, a story you may tell over and over again, highlighting, even inventing details. Other details fall away. You remember the light but not the heat, for instance, the tender kiss but not the clenched hand. The picture, while not complete, is focused and so memory has settled into a story that is always a kind of lie or, perhaps more fairly, as much fabrication as truth. On the other hand, it also takes time for memories to dissipate. Memories not committed to words, unwritten, unspoken, often become fuzzy and vague as if the brain cells themselves have remained undifferentiated, the imprint so slight that we ask ourselves, did this really happen or was it a dream? Perhaps I only imagined it.

And so it begins, even with the flight to Prague. My daughter and I changed planes in Heathrow but every time I think about that flight, I remember Paris, I think we changed planes in Paris. I *tell* people that the Charles de Gaulle airport was a zoo when, in fact, I have never been there, having only gone to Paris by train. But I do remember lines of people. A four-hour layover spent entirely in lines. In retrospect, I'm sure we had to go through Customs, pick up our checked luggage, make another trip through security, walk to another terminal, but the images in my mind—and it's only been a year, I am writing this only a year later—are already vague, in need of reconstruction. A hot crowded room that reminds me of a bus station. Three or four or five lines devoted to flights to Morocco? Tangiers? Some place in Africa? Dark-skinned people in bright clothing are speaking languages I've never heard, fanning themselves. Whole extended families. Trunks secured with ropes and tape. Aren't there glass windows with sunlight pouring through?

Kathryn is standing in another interminable line, her baseball cap pulled low over her eyes—we've already been traveling for twenty-one hours not counting time zone changes, twenty-one *real* hours, my watch is still on Tucson time—her backpack sagging with protein bars, bottled water, bags of nuts and dried fruit, chewing gum, cough drops, hand sanitizer, Kleenex, Band-Aids, toothbrushes and toothpaste, floss, moisturizer with sunscreen, two hoodies, umbrellas, my journal, pens, a guidebook with addresses and notes, a laminated street map, four magazines, a Ziploc bag full of menopause and period supplies (because you never know), another full of birth control pills, hormones, vitamins B and C, Xanax, decongestants, codeine, Ibuprofen, antihistamines, eyedrops, emery boards, tweezers, eyebrow pencil, mascara and ChapStick (do we think they don't have drugstores in Prague?), a change of underwear and a clean t-shirt for each of us. I am wearing the good backpack, the one with the padded shoulder straps and waistband, that also carries Kathryn's camera body and lenses. She is pulling behind her both of our suitcases; she is standing in the line she is sure we should be standing in.

But I am not sure. How do these milling people know where to go? Do we need boarding passes? Where do we get them? Where do we check our luggage? There are either no signs or I cannot read them. Is there an electronic check-in? I am standing with our tickets and itinerary behind two young men who are trying to negotiate with a woman behind a counter. The sign above her says *Billets*. Tickets. So I'm pretty sure she is in possession of the knowledge I need. She is speaking French. They are speaking French to her and some other language to one another. They are upset.

All I want to ask is: is that the right line for this ticket? But I will have to interrupt and, worse, I will have to interrupt in English, which will be, I know, unforgivable. *Pardon. Perdóname? Scusi. Excusez-moi?* In some part of my brain, there is a nook crammed full of Words-Not-English, but none of them means "boarding pass."

I look at Kathryn and shrug. She motions with her head for me to join her. She has been to Prague before; she has been to Beijing and Shanghai. Her sense of direction in Rome and New York City was infallible. I should trust her.

* * *

Barbara is sitting on the small balcony in Old Town when our taxi pulls up. She waves as if she were welcoming us to a palace. Dlouhá Street. There are a youth hostel and a club across the way, a stationer's, a used clothing store below on either side. The glass door to our entryway is cracked, the hallway dark and gray, the floors slick cement. The elevator is a wire cage with no door, an open fourth side, which makes me nervous. We crowd in with our luggage. Above us, the steel cable and pulley. We have come to a conference for writers and photographers where my friend Barbara teaches poetry. Kathryn studies the glass door as it slides shut. She is wondering about the light, I know, how it changes throughout the day. In our hallway, I catch a quick chill from Cold War ghosts and weeks later, when the door to another apartment is left open, I'll catch a glimpse of cramped gray quarters, old wool sweaters on a coat rack, tinge of cigarette smoke. But our apartment is full of light and blue furniture, polished wood floors. In the windows, floor to ceiling, white gauze curtains billow as if we are on the Mediterranean.

The streets seem full of people when we venture out. The cobbles, I feel them through my thin sandals. We follow Barbara, crossing—I'm sure, although I have no memory of doing so—the huge town square, passing below the Týn Church and the Astronomical Clock. We wind through narrow streets, past shops full of colorful wares and glaring lights, dioramas of commerce. People stream by us. I feel disoriented. Already exhausted from the flight and from weeks of taking care of my mother before the flight, I feel as if I've alighted on a surreal stage set and so I have a sudden sense of my own fragility. I'm sure my feet, in my thin sandals, will be bruised. I keep watching them navigate the cobbles. I will turn an ankle. This is my fear. There is no place smooth to walk. Girls are wearing flipflops and high heels. Slides with heels! This is what I'm thinking, of footwear, not of my mother whom I've left at home in a hospital, her eyes glittery with fever and pneumonia, a compression fracture of the spine. No, I'm worrying about footwear, that my feet will bruise, that strangers' heels will get wedged in the spaces between the cobbles.

Kathryn takes my hand and pulls me close to her. She links her arm through mine. She can feel my distraction. I am not quite here. And then we come around a dark corner to an opening. A street. Across it, a vista, the Charles Bridge, the black statues silhouetted just as you've seen in the postcards, the Charles Bridge against the light sky at dusk. People are streaming across, coming towards us; hundreds of people, it seems, are leaping across the street where the trolleys rattle. Are they trolleys? It is, Barbara declares, *almost* a perfect moment.

* * *

In the classroom, the teacher is saying that the subject matter must dictate the approach. You can't always get a single linear narrative. As in life, I think. The windows in the classroom are tall, wooden-framed, and when the wind comes, they bang against the sills. When traffic noise comes, a student gets up to close them.

The first morning, I had been late to class and, in my haste, had tripped going up the marble staircase, bruising my shins. A few weeks later, taking the garbage down into the basement of the apartment building, I will slip on the cement stairs, bruising my tailbone. It could have been a very bad fall, but I'd grabbed the railing, wrenching my shoulder to stop the momentum. The first fall was due, I know, to my new glasses and my haste and the second to the fact that I was wearing flipflops on cement as slick as ice—either fall could have happened to anyone—but I still come to think of both as emblematic of age, of my own aging, which I've never really felt before. That first morning, all eyes turned to me as I squeezed between the desks crammed together and made my way to the workshop table in the center of the room. The other students had to rearrange themselves to make a place for me. I could not have made a graceful entrance and so there is no reason I should have felt so disheveled and incompetent for mere tardiness, something I forgive others on a regular basis, but I did.

Most mornings I wish the teacher, with his large brown eyes and his expressive hands, would speak more loudly so we could keep the windows open and have some air. Perhaps he believes, as do the Navajo, that if you speak softly, people will listen more carefully. At break, I open the windows. The air here is oppressive with humidity. I feel it pushing against me, I can't get a clean breath, but I wonder if it's because of the river or just because I'm from the desert. Down on the street I see lines of people. They are waiting. There is a wall and they are waiting to go around a corner. And then I see over the wall, a cemetery. The Jewish cemetery. It must be the Jewish cemetery. Even from here, I see the thin gray headstones toppling towards one another like neglected teeth.

In the wide hallways, between classes, I stand at windows again. That's where I wait for Barbara and Cynthia so we can go to lunch at the Thai café, the hot, airless Thai café behind the shop that sells hand-blown glass, fantastic chandeliers that still look molten, tiny bubbles of air trapped forever, but we are the ones melting in the Thai café—not the beautiful waitresses in their silk dresses—no, we are the ones melting from the spicy food and hot air, the one fan turning, turning, turning but never towards us. I listen to my friends. I watch the people at other tables. Sometimes they order coffee. In this heat! I am the one who should have a camera.

Sometimes I wait before the windows in the hallway for a long time. I memorize the way the wooden doors look, I memorize the marble floors. Below the windows, there is a courtyard where people gather and smoke. Even in Bohemia one cannot smoke inside, this is my guess. One day, the photography students are lying on the ground. They are lying inside chalk drawings of human bodies. A crime scene? A teacher is standing on a chair directing them. He seems to think this is great fun. He waves at someone and I look across. There is a man standing directly across from me, in another hallway, in another window. He has a camera with a huge telephoto lens. He is taking a picture of the students. I have a sudden twinge of anxiety. I look for Kathryn. She is standing off to the side, watching. She wants no part of lying on the ground like a dead person.

* * *

Oddly, I am not worried that my mother will die while I'm in Prague. I believe she will wait for me. And this is true; she doesn't die. Instead she has an operation to stabilize her spine, she is treated for pneumonia and pumped full of morphine, which, my sister says over the crackling phone, makes her demented. They have to move her to a private room, for instance, because she insults the Jewish woman in the bed next to her. Or maybe it's the Indian woman she insults, or the Mexican—my husband Fernando cringes all the same. Over and over my mother dreams that she is on Saipan, where she and her husband were stationed in 1947. She dreams my older sister is a baby again and that they are surrounded by Japanese soldiers who have been hiding in the hills. Over and over she folds Kleenex, saying she is folding linen napkins for Kathryn's trousseau. Trousseau? It is not surprising that my mother loves such a word and loves the idea that Kathryn may someday marry someone who will expect her to have a trousseau and linen napkins.

* * *

One weekend, with other people from the conference, we take a field trip to Terezín. Even though touring a concentration camp seems to me at least slightly obscene, I tell myself it is a way of witnessing history. What is the alternative? Forgetting, ignoring what is just beneath the surface of time? Terezín, an old fortress, is itself halfway underground. The "bunk-rooms"—what else to call them?—in bunkers. Terezín was a holding camp or a transportation center, *not* a concentration camp, the guide tells us. Those who died here, she is careful to say once we are all ushered into the bunk-room, were not liquidated. They died of the conditions. Mostly children and the elderly were housed here and died here or were sent from here to their deaths in concentration camps. Auschwitz. Bergen-Belsen. A small bird flits from corner to corner of the ceiling, finally landing on the one small windowsill, so small and so high. (Someone, not Kathryn, it is too overtly symbolic for Kathryn, takes a picture of it.) The woman is saying numbers so incredible I know I will never remember them. One hundred? *Four* hundred slept in this room? The wooden platforms where they slept, no mattresses, no blankets, only so many centimeters allotted for each person. The cold showers, the elderly prisoners made to walk naked, wet, across snow-covered yards, from showers to bunks. Emaciated. Starving. Weak. But not liquidated. Not yet. (And, here, of course, I cannot help picturing my mother, her frail bones and thin blue veins, her sun-freckled skin, her modesty, my mother, her back hunched over, arms cradling her breasts, walking naked through the snow.) Pneumonia. Typhus, spread by lice. Tuberculosis, from the crowded conditions. All of this is told to us by a blonde woman in her early sixties, black and white print dress, in a soothing, lilting voice. She is solemn but it seems as if we are children, being told this information in the gentlest way possible. There is no horror in the recitation of these facts, no outrage, no emotional register in her voice at all. How many times does a person have to say the word "liquidation" in reference to human beings before the voice loses its emotional timbre? Did she stand before a mirror and practice?

Kathryn Alvarado, photograph

Kathryn and Bill have gone off, taking pictures; Pamela is writing everything down in a small black book, for her poetry, I guess. I am standing and trying to absorb this, to figure out how I am distancing myself from it. I feel nothing except for resistance to the woman, the woman who keeps herding us together for the recitation of the facts. There are: the bunks, the showers, the "fake bathroom" for the Red Cross and the media, the rooms where people were tortured, the round machines where clothing was washed but not at temperatures hot enough to kill lice. The beautiful grassy hill where the resistance workers were executed by firing squad four days before the war was over. The place where the escapee was publicly hanged. The place where three others successfully escaped. The long dark tunnel the resistance workers must have been led through to get to the hill where they were executed. The tunnel, the rough texture of its walls, the arched, barred windows in the corners where it changes directions. Kathryn hangs back to take pictures, the voices of the woman and the group receding, wafting back. Kathryn and I, alone, and I am suddenly afraid, not of ghosts but of sensing them, of feeling what they felt. There is something in the air, something unmistakable, something sacred. You can't believe they didn't know. You can't believe they walked through that long dark twisting tunnel, that they stepped out into sunlight and green grass and didn't know.

In the museum we see the art by the children and their teachers. Some of the children survived but none of the teachers did. And later, the crematorium that still smells of ash. The room that looks like a medical room—the shiny stainless steel operating table, the white enamel sink; this particularly bothers me because I remember reading about experiments performed on live prisoners without anesthesia—although that did not happen at Terezín as far as I know. As far as we know, according to the guide's lilting voice, only the dead were cremated here, not the living, only the bodies. Still, at the sight of the table I suddenly feel my heart constrict, my first physiological response, other than the panicked claustrophobia in the tunnel.

There is an older man on the tour. He iss traveling with his daughter—she is in her 50's, he in his late 70's, early 80's, I'd guess. He is having a difficult time emotionally. It seems to me that they are speaking Czech but also she speaks at times in English, the language flowing from sounds I cannot understand into sounds I can, like an image coming fleetingly into focus. When he emerges from the crematorium, he clutches at his heart, his eyes are tearing, as they have been at several other points in the tour. I think maybe he is going to have a heart attack. I think maybe I am observing his emotional reactions to distance myself from my own. I knew my father had been cremated, I knew my mother wanted to be, but it was only a word until I smell the ash. I swear, you could smell the ash. Is it possible? And I wonder if I can feel compassion only when there was a one-to-one correlation. Does this mean there is something wrong with me? That I could be one of those people who could compartmentalize, who could deny the humanity of others?

I am standing outside, composing myself by looking at the trees, the clouds building above us. I am thinking of Arendt's *Eichmann in Jerusalem,* the banality of evil, of Sontag's *Regarding the Pain of Others,* of Celan's poem, "black milk of daybreak we drink you at night . . .". Perhaps everything has to be mediated for me through language. Images, it seems to me, even photographs, are immediate, visceral, disturbing. Maybe the image, even when it's secondhand, an artifact, is imprinted in a primitive portion of the brain, a lobe that registers emotion or pain, that says, danger! run! Whereas language, like air, is literally taken into the body and so must be absorbed, must circulate with oxygen molecules in the blood, must become a part of the brain and, in that process, can somehow soften, dissipate, transform, from raw emotion to meaning, abstraction. But then how to account for the difference between the phrases "banality of evil" and "black milk of daybreak"—even how and where they register in the body—since they are both language?

This is a silly thing to be wondering about as I watch Charlotte walk down the long dirt road back to the bus by herself. She has not gone into the crematorium. Her husband died of cancer only months before and she had washed his body herself and wound him in a cloth and made a death mask, but this is too much for her to bear. I do not go to her. (Cynthia does. Pamela does.) I do not ask her if she was okay. I do not know if I would ever be able to take care of the dead or even the dying. There is something repulsive about the decline of the body, about decay. I don't want to be the person who notices that the old man smells of urine, but I am. I watch him light a cigarette. I watch Kathryn and Bill as they take pictures of a tree the children had planted as a memorial when the camp was liberated. The tree is dead now, its trunk and several huge limbs still standing stark and bare against the background of green, the line of living trees behind it.

* * *

As I'm sitting in the airless Bohemia Bagel Shop and Internet Café, I open emails from Fernando: Your mother is recovering. Thinks she's surrounded by Japanese soldiers. Lyn goes home tomorrow. Kay arrives Friday. Love to Kat. To you, too.

When I recite them to Kathryn, I insert the word "stop" wherever there's a period: Your mother is recovering—*stop*—Thinks she's surrounded by Japanese soldiers—*stop*. We laugh. I feel almost giddy because none of this is my responsibility.

I cannot yet know that guilt is inevitable and will hit as soon as the airliner's tires hit the tarmac in Tucson. I cannot imagine the plans my mother will devise to escape skilled nursing and go back to her townhouse. I'm going AMA on Monday, she will cheerily tell the nurses, my son is coming to take me home. AMA. Against Medical Advice.

How can I imagine that my brother will need to believe her stories, need to believe that I abandoned her, almost killed her by putting her in the hospital? But this is his necessary fiction, the son as savior. She will persuade him to rescue her by telling him the story about *her* brother Rees: when he found their mother in a nursing home, he walked in, picked her up right out of the bed, carried her out to his car and took her home. This, of course, as my mother knows, appeals to the romantic in my brother.

*First plan*: he will come in an RV, she tells me, and drive her all the way to Colorado. All the way across the Indian Reservation, I will ask her, with an oxygen tank? What happens if you break down?

*Second plan*: he will come in a Lincoln Continental, she says, which has the smoothest ride ever, and take her to her townhouse. Who will take care of you there? I ask her. Phillip has to go back to Colorado. Lyn and Kay live in Colorado. Mom? I can't. I can't take care of you any longer.

How can I know I will be forced to be the wicked daughter, the one who has to tell her mother the truth, that she will never be well enough to go home, never be well enough to live independently again. *Who will take care of you?* I am the one who will have to ask her this. She is sitting in her wheelchair next to the window. She is worrying a Kleenex to shreds.

If Phillip comes in here and takes you AMA, I tell her, they can call the police.

Will they arrest me, too? she asks. Think I'm guilty of collusion?

Mom, I tell her, they're not going to put *you* in jail, but I know you don't want to see Phil get in trouble.

*Phil?* she says, placing her open palm against her heart emphatically. *Phil?* (Again with the hand.) *I'm* the one we're supposed to be worried about here.

She is the one we're supposed to be worried about. Oh, how I will chastise myself as I lie in bed at night. Ungrateful, selfish girl. *How sharper than a serpent's tooth. . . .* But Phil doesn't know the rest of the story, how no one could provide proper care for my grandmother, how she ended up in a nursing home again, where she died, stroke by stroke.

Of course this story, the real story, was never told to me when I was a child either. No, when I was a child I heard only the story of how my mother cared for her own mother, brushing her hair, day after day, the dutiful daughter giving up everything, even her singing, her art, for her mother. This is the story that will wake me up in the middle of the night in a panic. How can I abandon my mother? How can I choose my life over hers? But I will. And in calmer moments, I will know it is what she would have me do.

* * *

Barbara and I spend an afternoon just off Old Town Square in the Kinsky Palace, a pink building built in the eighteenth century, although once inside, you see remnants of the older building dating from the fourteenth century. History is literally built on history, the buildings of a city, a kind of palimpsest if you know how to read stones or the sedimentary layers of human industry. Here, inside, the stone walls—I remember curved stone walls but perhaps they were brick—Barbara and I pause in a small courtyard where, we agree, it would be perfect to have an iced tea, and then up the stairs to the National Gallery, its hallways and rooms filled with art and a hush not unlike that in a cathedral. *Art Brut.* Not all the artists were mental patients; some were recluses, their work found later in dusty, abandoned apartments. Many paintings were dream images, the eyes often haunting or frightening. Some reminded me of Basquiat, angular, bestial, primary colors. Words as images. Their materials: ink, pen, crayon, pencil, pharmaceuticals, blood, collage, paper bags, pictures torn from magazines. One whole section of the exhibit was about the body, alienation from the body, fears about the body, fears about sex, fears about dismemberment, fears about penetration, fears about the death of the body, and, of course, fears about the decay of the body. The artists' stories were printed on sheets of paper. Many had been abandoned as children or had suffered through the trauma of war. *Art Brut.* Raw Art. Visions of a chaotic world.

* * *

In the evenings, Old Town Square is filled with soccer fans waving flags. The TV is as large as the screen at an outdoor movie theatre. Barbara leads Kathryn and me through the winding cobblestone streets, over the bridge, which can't be the Charles Bridge because we stop to gaze at the Charles Bridge, its distinctive statues dark in the bluish twilight. We gaze at the bridge and the glassy water and the birds swooping. We take a tram up to the hills west of the Vltava River and are deposited in a neighborhood that is much quieter than Old Town, more residential. Perhaps it is the Ukrainian District: there are so many shops with icons. We pass two young Asian girls, maybe in their late teens, early twenties. The one in the lead seems drunk, she is singing and swaying as she walks; the one following is pensive, perhaps angry or worried. Down the hill we walk. We stop at an outdoor restaurant in front of the monastery, the white tables set out in a row on the edge of a hill overlooking all of Prague. There is a breeze, the moon is peeking over the hills just to our right. We are even above the castle and the cathedral, which are below us to our left; directly below lies Prague, the bridges and the Týn church in Old Town barely recognizable from this distance. We order ice cream and water.

Because this is a perfect moment, as Barbara would say, the kind of moment my mother would want me to have in Europe, I call her at the skilled nursing facility where she is recovering. Her voice is crackling or wispy; perhaps it is not a good connection. I walk over away from the tables, into the shadows, turn this way and that as if I am an antenna. I describe for her the moon, the castle, the river, the town square full of soccer fans. She says, I called my sister Elizabeth. I told her you put me in a nursing home so you could take off for Europe.

My mother. I'd wondered how long it would take for that version of events to become her story. But of course, my sister said, but of course, Fernando laughed, that would be the story. What did you expect? *Beth put me in a nursing home*—stop—*she took off for Europe*—stop—*come save me*—

* * *

Sometimes in the hot afternoons, I sit in the shade at da Nico's, a café with a green awning about two blocks from our apartment. I sit in the shade, near the fan, and drink an iced café au lait. The waitress, a young woman with her hair in a long blonde braid, wants to know, precisely, how much milk, how much sugar? I wonder if preferences vary according to nationality. It makes me feel that Americans must be picky and that I must seem American, since she is anxious about pleasing me, and that, therefore, she must think I am picky. I am careful to praise the coffee and to leave a good tip. I always feel like an outsider in America, which is okay with me, but when I am in other countries, I feel very American. Case in point: the last time I was in Paris, 2004, Bush was visiting. The headline in *Le Monde:* "All of Europe Grits its Teeth." I carried *Le Monde* in my bag. I told Fernando we should speak to one another in Spanish while in cafés or on buses. I was tempted to take up smoking again, preferably Gauloise. As a general rule, I like the disconnect of not-belonging, of feeling invisible, of being a voyeur. I like being surrounded by languages I don't understand. It allows me to exist in the world in a way in which I am comfortable: not quite *of* it. Perhaps no one expects anything of me. And so maybe I could do it. Cut myself free. Never go home. Rent a small apartment in Prague. Teach English as a foreign language. Become an ex-pat. Live the life of the mind. Maybe I am not too old, maybe it is not too late to choose another existence. Maybe no one would miss me.

* * *

The bar is small and dark and smoky. A few nights before Kathryn and her friend Stephanie had gone to a five-story disco down by the river, but tonight we go out for a few drinks with the waiter from da Nico's and the cook. It's right around the corner from our apartment. Phat Boy's, where the locals hang out. The waiter is a little guy—handsome, according to Stephanie—with short dark hair, a fringe of bleached blond in the very front. The cook is a big guy, shaved head, two huge plugs in his earlobes. I've seen him in the kitchen. The waiter lives an hour out from the restaurant. He makes 15,000 crowns a month, or about $600. He says you make more only if you are a professional, an office worker, or work for the government. He says the manager of the restaurant—a slight guy with one wandering eye who waited on us the first night—has two faces. One is smiling, the other is mean. Or two tongues, is how Stephanie, her own hair black and spiky, red hoop earrings, will later remember it—as we lounge on the blue couch in our apartment's blue living room—two sides to his mouth. The manager is a photographer and his prints of street scenes in Afghanistan hang on the walls in the no-smoking dining room. They are printed on large squares of fabric. In one, people are walking and the pigeons at their feet are caught taking flight, the blur of wings, motion arrested, that is what appeals to me.

Milan, the cook, likes good tequila and keeps disappearing to other neighboring bars in his quest to find some Jo-say Cuvaro which, he informs us, is *primo*. Patrón? Kathryn asks. El Jimador? I'm Mexican, I'm from Arizona, and I've never heard of Jo-say Cuvaro. But the cook has disappeared again on his quest before we realize that Jo-say Cuvaro is, perhaps, Czech for José Cuervo. Does he ever return? None of us can remember but we do remember his friend from childhood who joined us about halfway through the evening. He has long hair and is very drunk or else on drugs. He has a photograph he wants to show us: his face, profile, distorted. He had placed his face on a Xerox machine and this was his self-portrait. The waiter has a second job, which is finding girls who want to be dancers. He hooks them up with this man who sends them to other countries: Britain, Japan. They make a lot of money, he says, and in some countries there are very strict laws about not touching the dancers. London is mentioned, but later we are not sure if London has strict laws or not or if it has strict laws but they aren't enforced. In Japan, the men want to have sex with the dancers. We remember this. David, the waiter, sees nothing wrong with providing this service—the girls want to go, they make money, he makes money. The service was started by a man from the U. S., he tells us. An entrepreneur. Stupid fucking Americans, the cook's drunk friend says. Stupid fucking Americans, they only know stupid fucking American bands. You girls like drugs, sex, rock and roll? You girls like Nirvana?

* * *

My mother hadn't wanted us to come to Prague, dark sooty land of Communists. She was afraid Kathryn would be kidnapped by sex-slave traders. In the hospital, she took both of my hands in hers. She made me promise to keep Kathryn safe. Don't you let her out of your sight for a minute, she told me, both hands clutching mine. She paused. But don't you bring her home early. Not even if I die.

We held hands and I promised to keep Kathryn safe and she promised not to die and we felt as if saying it aloud would make it true. She had always said, show me you love me. Don't tell me. Words mean nothing. And I have tried to show her, by taking care of her. She had begun introducing me as her devoted daughter—this is Beth, my daughter, she is *devoted* to me—and, here, she would insert some detail about how bossy I am. And even though she was joking—because, really, who ever would have thought we could be so close? so much the same?—it was her way of saying, I know it's been hard for you. I've needed you. I appreciate what you've done.

* * *

In Prague, I am outside of time, in some other reality, my perceptions heightened by extreme emotion or travel or heat or sleeplessness. I stand in front of the long windows of our apartment; I part the white gauze curtains and look up and down the street for my daughter. It is three a.m. I have dreamed my mother, emaciated, helpless on the stainless steel table, and I cannot fall back to sleep. I stand before the long windows in my nightgown. Across the street, a youth hostel, a club. Behind windows like mine, young people come and go, up and down a staircase beneath a red neon arrow. They sit on couches. They watch TV, smoke cigarettes, drink beer. Kiss, occasionally. Outside on the street, men stand next to their taxis. It is summer. Everyone is drunk and exuberant with noise. Teenaged boys run through the streets, waving flags, calling out *Deutschland, Deutschland*. I am in a country where I don't speak the languages, I can't sleep without dreaming of my mother's bones, and my daughter, where is she? I have promised to keep her safe. Maybe she's around the corner. In a bar with her friends. Maybe at the discothèque on the river. Where? I don't know. I stand in the window and watch for her, imagine myself walking the cobblestone streets, trying to find her. Imagine myself talking to people who do not understand me. Their mouths move in ways I cannot decipher. I place my open hand above my heart to calm it. I stand in the window and the taxi drivers below wave to me; they are so used to seeing me there, in my black nightgown, waiting.

* * *

In the classroom, I am sitting next to the teacher. He is very famous and, although I am perhaps only a decade or so younger than he is, I cannot bring myself to call him by his first name. Some of the other students do, but it seems presumptuous to me. I'm not sure why, but I remember that we are sitting on a couch. It now seems impossible that there was a couch in the classroom, but that's what I remember, we're sitting side by side, looking slightly to our left so we can see out the window that is just above the Jewish cemetery. If this were fiction, I would place a coffee table in front of us and cups of coffee in our hands or glasses of wine. Maybe I would just go ahead and put us in a living room or at a dining room table because, although I do not call him by his first name, it seems as if we are old friends, sitting there, musing about writing, about the difficulty of reflection, why it is nearly impossible under certain circumstances.

The question is not what happens, he has said in class, but what the writer makes of it: reflection provides an essential counter-narrative, an ongoing dialectic between past and present. My writing, I know, is too photographic for him. I am not interpreting for my readers. I am simply recording. He does not say this, but I assume it's what he thinks and, because we are so *simpatico* in this moment, I am probably right. He has said that life has an underlying shape and that the writer's job is to discover the shape—perhaps like a sculptor releasing the figure from the stone? I'm not sure I believe this, I tell him. Life has a shape? Writing for me is more like creating a room, a scene from the stuff of life. I want the reader to enter the room and so to enter the dream. Memory as a room; fiction as a continuous dream. But we are talking about nonfiction, he reminds me. For him, there is a clear distinction.

And then the thing I remember next also seems impossible, but I remember looking with him at Kathryn's proofsheets from Terezín. So many doors, I say, there were so many doors. Doors behind archways, doors behind bars and grids of bars, interior doors that lead nowhere.

See? I run my fingers over the proofsheet.

I know he has said that a photographic style actually distances the reader because it creates a fragmented approach. Like the use of present tense, he has said, verbal snapshots mean we never get to the life underneath.

Oh, the life underneath, the examined life. I think I am too tired from living, right now, to go there. Perhaps, it occurs to me, I write the way I do because I want to distance myself, to escape. I want to take things I've felt deeply and make of them beautiful, external objects. I want to create an image that in the hue of its colors, in the way light falls, in its lines and shapes and sounds, gives rise to the emotions beneath its surface. Maybe, I think, I should have been a painter. Or a poet.

I look at the proofsheets, the long hallways full of doors half-opened, the windows behind bars, windows the shape of doors, windows and doors which are not openings, windows and doors which are sealed with heavy iron bars, doors the texture of tombstones, tombstones shaped like doors.

* * *

Four months after we return, my mother will fall and break her hip and during the surgery, against her wishes, she will be intubated. In the hospital room, I will turn and see Kathryn's face close to my mother's, they are holding hands. Kathryn leans in to whisper so my mother can hear her, and the nurse says to me, Oh, they look so much alike! Your daughter looks so much like your mother. But it is their spirits we see. It is Kathryn who will say what I cannot say: I cherish you and I know you cherish me. When she touches me, my mother told me once, I feel it in her hands. She loves me unconditionally. She is the only one. All of this is what I think and do not say as I see their faces together. Kathryn and I have been sitting, each of us on either side of my mother's bed, each of us holding a hand. I have promised my mother that we will abide by her wishes, we will make them remove the breathing tube. I have the strength, I tell her, because of you. Her eyes, she closes her eyes then. Rests. She knows I will do what she wants. Fernando's warm hand in the middle of my back at night comforts me. The spirit is of the body. It needs the body. To see, to hear, to touch. This is why every death feels like a kind of violence.

* * *

The entryway, the three-sided elevator, the blue living room; the lady across the street in the apartment above the hostel, tending her geraniums, hanging her laundry in the window. Memory as a place, as an object. Kat's and my room, the explosion of clothes from our suitcases, camera equipment hidden in clothes, the red netted curtains beneath the white gauze; Barbara's back bedroom with the leaky ceiling and small porch for drying clothes; gardens with hydrangea below; apartment balconies across the way; everyone smokes. "The moment we step into the space of memory," Paul Auster writes, "we walk into the world." The sidewalks of small white cobbles, some of which are used in our apartment as window stops; the white inlaid crosses in Old Town Square, twenty-seven, one for each martyr beheaded upon that spot; the clockmaker, blinded by the townspeople, so he couldn't go to Germany and make another clock; defenestration, Cynthia tells me, from *fenêtre,* window in French, defenestration, which means to throw someone out of a high castle window, especially during political upheaval, as in a coup. Liquidation, which means only one thing. "In the struggle between yourself and the world, you must side with the world," Kafka said, but I don't think Kafka had children, could have imagined, even in his darkest hours, Terezín. Lunches in the Thai café behind the glass shop, the air molten; readings at night in the theatre below the smoke-filled bar; Le Louvre Café, the garden dining room on the roof, the other buildings around us still taller so it wasn't as if we were on a roof at all; the bridge, the light at dusk, honey-colored, later blue; the John Lennon memorial; the shadowy sculptures of people climbing stairs to a garden as we were saying goodbye to Cynthia; the discussion of "the fragment" after Cynthia and Barbara's readings. I cherish you and I know you cherish me, Kathryn will say, and it already echoes in the blue living room, in the blue living room, where Barbara brings the carved wooden turtle in from the narrow balcony and places it on the TV so we'll have a pet; where she arranges chairs on our precarious balcony so we'll have a beach; where she balances a glass of red wine on the window sill as she asks me, are we going to accept the terms of the piece or ask the writer to set up new terms?

## About the Authors

Richard Agacinski writes poetry and fiction; as Richard C. Allen, he has taught religious studies, philosophy, and English literature, published scholarly articles and a book, *David Hartley on Human Nature* (1999).

Beth Alvarado memoir, *Anthropologies*, is forthcoming from University of Iowa Press this fall. Her story collection, *Not a Matter of Love*, was published by New Rivers Press. Other recent work appears in *Sonora Review, Western Humanities Review, North American Review, Seattle Review, Third Coast,* and the anthology, *Dedicated to the People of Darfur*. She teaches at the University of Arizona.

Rebecca Baggett's chapbook, *God Puts on the Body of a Deer*, was recently released by Main Street Rag. The title poem was nominated for a Pushcart Prize and "Alleluia," another poem in the collection, won *Atlanta Review*'s 2010 International Poetry Competition. Her next collection, *Thalassa*, is forthcoming. She lives in Athens, Georgia, where she works as an academic advisor for the Franklin College of Arts and Sciences at the University of Georgia.

Erinn Batykefer is the author of *Allegheny, Monongahela* (2009), winner of the Benjamin Saltman Poetry Prize. Her poetry and nonfiction have appeared recently in *FIELD, Prairie Schooner, Sou'wester, Nimrod,* and *Devils Lake.* She is currently at work on a second collection and a memoir.

Richard N. Bentley has published fiction and poetry on three continents. He has two books out currently, *Post Freudian Dreaming* and *A General Theory of Desire.* He served on the board of the Modern Poetry Association (now known as the Poetry Foundation), and was a prizewinner in *The Paris Review*/Paris Writers Workshop International Fiction Awards. Before teaching creative writing at the University of Massachusetts, he served as Chief Planner for the Mayor's Office of Housing in Boston.

Michael Biggins's book-length translations of works by Slovene poet Tomaž Šalamun and novelists Vladimir Bartol, Drago Jančar and Boris Pahor have been published by Harcourt, Northwestern University Press and others. He curates the Slavic and East European library collections and teaches Slavic languages at the University of Washington in Seattle.

Michael Boccardo's poems have appeared or are forthcoming in *Hayden's Ferry Review, RATTLE, RHINO, Southern Poetry Review, The Southern Review, Cutthroat,* and elsewhere. His honors include a prize from the Dorothy Sargent Rosenburg Foundation and an honorable mention in the Joy Harjo Poetry Prize. He resides in High Point, North Carolina, serving as an editorial assistant for *Cave Wall,* while currently employed as a merchandise manager with Barnes & Noble.

MICHELLE BRITTAN has been published in *CALYX,* and is the title poet for *Time You Let Me In,* an anthology of young poets edited by Naomi Shihab Nye. Born in San Francisco of mixed white and Malaysian heritage, she is a candidate in the M.F.A. program at California State University, Fresno, where she recently won an Academy of American Poets prize judged by Philip Levine. She currently teaches undergraduate poetry, co-edits the student-run *San Joaquin Review,* and interns with *The Normal School.*

CLIFFORD BROWDER's poetry has appeared in *Heliotrope, Runes, Snake Nation Review, The Same,* and elsewhere. He is also author of two published biographies and a critical study of the French Surrealist poet André Breton. His historical novel *The Pleasuring of Men* will be published in 2011 by Gival Press.

CORY BROWN has published three collections of poems; his work has appeared in *BOMB, Northwest Review, Postmodern Culture,* and *West Branch,* and is forthcoming in *Arroyo, The Antigonish Review, The Fiddlehead, Haiku Ramblings,* and *Sentence.* He grew up raising cattle in Oklahoma and teaches writing at Ithaca College, in upstate New York.

ELIZABETH BULL's fiction has appeared in *Gulf Coast* and *Third Coast,* and is forthcoming in *H.O.W. Journal.* She earned an M.F.A. in Creative Writing from The New School in New York and a B.A. in Film from the UCLA School of Theater, Film, and Television. She also studied filmmaking at the Dun Laoghaire Institute of Art and Design in Dublin, Ireland, on a Rotary International Scholarship. Elizabeth currently teaches at the University of Zadar in Croatia through the Fulbright Program.

CHRIS BULLARD lives in Collingswood, New Jersey, and works for the federal government as an administrative law judge. He attended the University of Pennsylvania and is currently enrolled in the writing program at Wilkes University. His work has appeared in *Green Mountains Review, Nimrod, Pleiades, River Styx,* and other literary magazines. One of his sonnets was featured in the recent Tribute to the Sonnet issue of *RATTLE.* In 2009, Plan B Press published his chapbook, *You Must Not Know Too Much.*

CAROL V. DAVIS won the 2007 T.S. Eliot Prize for *Into the Arms of Pushkin: Poems of St. Petersburg.* She was twice a Fulbright scholar in Russia and teaches at Santa Monica College, California. Her poetry has been in *Ploughshares, Prairie Schooner,* and *Hayden's Ferry Review* and is forthcoming in *Natural Bridge.*

Rafaella Del Bourgo's writing has appeared in journals such as *WordWrights, Caveat Lector, Puerto Del Sol, RATTLE, The New York Quarterly,* and *The Bitter Oleander.* She has won many awards, including Pushcart nominations in 2002 and 2006. She won the Lullwater Prize for Poetry in 2003, the Helen Pappas Prize in Poetry and the New River Poets Award in 2006, First Place in the Maggi Meyer Poetry Competition in 2007. Her first collection of poetry, *I Am Not Kissing You,* was published in 2003.

Nicole DiCello's work has appeared in publications such as *Poetry East, The Mid-America Poetry Review, Nimrod, Concho River Review,* and *Ballard Street Poetry Journal.* Her manuscript *Redshift* was a finalist for the 2008 Bordighera Poetry Prize. She is an M.F.A. candidate in the Creative Writing Poetry program at Emerson College and a reader for *Ploughshares.*

Robert Dugan is an Assistant Professor at Keystone College in Northeast Pennsylvania. A Shakespeare scholar, he finds that writing poetry helps keep him honest and grounded in pursuit of the persistent mystery of this life.

Susan Elbe is the author of *Eden in the Rearview Mirror* and a chapbook, *Light Made from Nothing.* Her poems appear or are forthcoming in many journals and anthologies, including *Blackbird, diode, MARGIE, North American Review, Salt Hill,* and *A Fierce Brightness: Twenty-five Years of Women's Poetry.* Among her awards are the inaugural Lois Cranston Memorial Poetry Prize from *CALYX,* the 2006 Lorine Niedecker Award, and fellowships to Vermont Studio Center and Virginia Center for Creative Arts.

Paul Fisher earned an M.F.A. in poetry from New England College and has studied writing in a variety of academic and workshop settings, including the University of Washington, Centrum, and the Writer's Center in Bethesda, Maryland. He is the recipient of an Individual Artist's Fellowship in Poetry from the Oregon Arts Commission. His first full-length book, *Rumors of Shore,* won the 2009 Blue Light Book Award.

Mary Gilliland lives in Ithaca, New York. Her recent poetry has also appeared in *AGNI, Chautauqua, Hotel Amerika, Notre Dame Review, Stand, Tygerburning,* and in *The &NOW Awards: The Best Innovative Writing.* She was a featured reader at the 5th International Al Jazeera Festival in Doha, Qatar.

Jonathan Greenhause's poetry has appeared in more than a hundred literary reviews around the world, most recently in *Borderlands, cream city review, Interim,* and *Roanoke Review,* and has been nominated for a Pushcart

Prize. He works as a Spanish interpreter and lives with his stand-up comic wife and their dog, Antigone.

VICTORIA GIVOTOVSKY's poems have appeared in *Birmingham Poetry Review, Natural Bridge, RATTLE, Runes*, and *The Bitter Oleander*, among other journals. Her chapbook, *Elegies and Other Love Songs*, was published in 2006 by toadlily press.

MARYLEN GRIGAS lives and writes in Burlington, Vermont. After years of teaching high school and college English and drama, she currently works in her family's architectural stained glass studio. Her poems have been published in journals including *MARGIE: The American Journal of Poetry, Poetry East, Iodine Poetry Journal,* and *The Pedestal Magazine.*

JUSTIN HAMM's writing has appeared or will soon appear in *cream city review, The New York Quarterly, Spoon River Poetry Review, Red Rock Review, The Brooklyn Review,* and numerous other publications. Recent work has also been featured on the Indiefeed: Performance Poetry channel and has been nominated for the Pushcart Prize.

M. MICHAEL HANNER graduated from University of Illinois and lived in Chicago until moving to Oregon in 1970, where he worked as an architect for 35 years. He is a member of Red Sofa Poets. His poetry has appeared in *Cloudbank, Crab Creek Review, Denali, Tiger's Eye, MARGIE, Mudfish*, the CD *Poets Demanding Ink* and several anthologies. He has published a number of chapbooks, including the most recent *Closing Down the Piccolo Bar* (2008) and *Palm Sunday* (2009).

KRISTEN INGRID HOGGATT, after receiving her B.A. from the University of Arizona, served in Uzbekistan with the Peace Corps, where she had the rewarding experience of facilitating a poetry workshop. She received her M.F.A. from Emerson College and is the author of the biweekly "Ask a Poet" advice column for Drexel University's *The Smart Set*. Her poetry has appeared in *The Ledge Magazine, The Healing Muse*, and *Alligator Juniper*.

KAREN HOLMBERG is a poet and creative nonfiction writer whose work has appeared or is forthcoming in such magazines as *Quarterly West, Southern Poetry Review, West Branch, Cave Wall, Potomac Review, Black Warrior Review, New Madrid, Poetry East*, and *Cimarron Review*. She teaches in the M.F.A. program at Oregon State University.

WILLIAM HORRELL is a retired professor of Humanities with degrees in English and philosophy from the University of Illinois at Chicago and the University of Arkansas in Fayetteville. His most recent academic work has appeared in *The Wordsworth Circle*. He lives in Kingston, Arkansas, with his wife, botanical artist Kate Nessler.

JODI L. HOTTEL is a writer and retired English teacher, living in Santa Rosa, California. Her work has been published in the *English Journal, The Dickens, Frogpond,* and anthologies from the University of Iowa Press, Tebot Bach, and the Healdsburg Arts Council. She is currently working on her first chapbook, a gathering of poems about the Japanese American internment.

KITTY JOSPÉ is a French teacher and art docent, with a passion for language, people, and all the arts. She holds an M.A. in French Literature from New York University and an M.F.A. in Poetry from Pacific University, Oregon. Her first book, *Cadences,* was released in March 2010 by Foothills publishing.

LIZ KAY holds an M.F.A. from the University of Nebraska, where she was the recipient of both an Academy of American Poets Prize and the Wendy Fort Foundation Prize. Recent poems have appeared in such journals as *Redactions: Poetry & Poetics, The New York Quarterly, Iron Horse Literary Review, Willow Springs,* and *Sugar House Review.*

SUSANNE KORT's poetry, prose, and translations have appeared in *Grand Street, North American Review, New Orleans Review, Puerto del Sol, Indiana Review, Green Mountains Review, Notre Dame Review, The Antioch Review,* and other journals in the U.S., Canada, the Caribbean, the U.K., and Ireland. She is a psychotherapist practicing in Jalisco, Mexico.

JACQUELINE KUDLER teaches classes in memoir writing and literature at the College of Marin in Kentfield, CA. She serves as an advisory director on the board of Marin Poetry Center and is a founding member of Sixteen Rivers Press. Her poems have appeared in numerous reviews, magazines, and anthologies; her poetry collection, *Sacred Precinct,* was published in 2003. She was awarded the Marin Arts Council Board Award in 2005 and the Marin Poetry Center Lifetime Achievement Award in 2010.

ERICA LEHRER is a Houston-based poet, journalist, fiction writer, and former practicing attorney. Her writing has appeared in national and regional publications. She is a graduate of Princeton University and New York University School of Law. Lehrer received a grant from Vermont Studio Center for Summer 2010 and spent her time there working on *Dancing with Ataxia,* a collection of poetry informed by a rare degenerative condition with which she has been recently diagnosed.

NORMAN LOCK is the author of seven books of fiction, including the novels *A History of the Imagination* (FC2), *The Land of the Snow Men* (Calamari Press), *Shadowplay* (Ellipsis Press), *The Long Rowing Unto Morning* and *The King of Sweden* (Ravenna Press). He has also written for the stage and for German radio. He is a recipient of the Aga Khan Prize given by *The Paris Review* and prose fellowships from the New Jersey and the Pennsylvania State Councils on the Arts.

NICHOLAS MAISTROS attends the M.F.A. Program for Fiction at Colorado State University. His stories and essays have earned him publication in the *Bellingham Review,* second place in the 2010 *Gulf Coast* Prize, and admission to The Bread Loaf Writers' Conference. He is currently at work on a book of linked essays.

DEBRA McCALL, who lives and works in the greater Tulsa area, practices a fusion style of healing arts that incorporates, therapeutic bodywork, interior design, feng shui, creative writing, and sound and movement therapies. Her work has appeared in various journals since 1995.

MARYANN FRANTA MOENCK lives and writes just east of St. Paul, Minnesota. Her poems have been published online in *Three Candles, The Pedestal, The Literary Bohemian,* and other sites. Her print publications include pieces in *Snowy Egret, Cimarron Review, Natural Bridge,* and *Water-Stone Review*. She serves as a poetry reader for *Bosphorus Art Project Quarterly,* and works as an administrative assistant for the White Bear Center for the Arts. The rhythm of a long walk is her favorite writing catalyst.

JENNIFER ANNE MOSES is the author of *Food and Whine* and *Bagels and Grits.* Her short stories have been widely published in litererary magazines, and have also appeared in *The Pushcart Prizes* and *New Stories from the South: The Year's Best.* She lives with her husband, dogs, and children in Montclair, New Jersey, where she also paints.

JED MYERS is a Seattle poet whose work appears or is forthcoming in *Golden Handcuffs Review, Atlanta Review, Prairie Schooner, Fugue,* and elsewhere. He's had editorial roles with *Tufts Literary Magazine, Chrysanthemum,* and *Drash.* He is a psychiatrist with a therapy practice and teaches at the University of Washington.

KENNETH O'KEEFE is a retired public school teacher who resides in Pittsburgh. The poem appearing in this issue emerged from his memory of an actual occurrence.

ANNE M. DOE OVERSTREET works as a freelance editor and a private gardener. Her poems have appeared in *Asheville Poetry Review, DMQ Review,*

*Relief, Talking River Review, Cranky,* and elsewhere. A nominee for the Pushcart Prize, she lives in Shoreline, Washington.

THOMAS PATTERSON is a past contributor to *Nimrod (Memory: Lost and Found)* and his poems have appeared in numerous journals, including *Confrontation, Chiron Review*, and *Plainsongs*. Two new poems appear in the e-zine version of *Cavalier Literary Couture*; other new work will appear this spring in *The South Carolina Review* and *Cider Press Review*.

ADAM PENNA is the author of *Little Songs & Lyrics to Genji* (2010) and *The Love of a Sleeper* (2008). His work has appeared such journals as *Cimarron Review, Cider Press Review, Think Journal,* and *Verse Daily*.

EMILY PÉREZ holds an M.F.A. from the University of Houston. Her poetry has appeared in *The Laurel Review, /nor, DIAGRAM*, and *Borderlands*, and her reviews can be found in *Gulf Coast* and *Latino Poetry Review*. Her manuscript was recently a finalist for the Montoya Prize given by the University of Notre Dame. She currently lives in Seattle where she teaches English and poetry writing.

ANDREA POTOS's poetry collections include *Yaya's Cloth* (Iris Press) and *The Perfect Day* (Parallel Press). Two poetry collections are forthcoming: *Abundance to Share With the Birds* (Finishing Line Press) and *We Lit the Lamps Ourselves* (Salmon Poetry). She lives in Madison, Wisconsin, with her husband and daughter.

DIAN DUCHIN REED is the author of *Medusa Discovers Styling Gel* (Finishing Line Press, 2009). Recent poems appear in *Prairie Schooner, Poet Lore,* and *Poetry East*. She has been the recipient of a Sundberg Family grant for literary criticism, the Mel Tuohey Award for writing excellence, and the Mary Lonnberg Smith Award in Poetry.

MARY KAY RUMMEL's sixth poetry book, *What's Left Is The Singing*, was published by Blue Light Press in 2010. Other recent poetry books are *Love in the End* (2008) and *The Illuminations* (2006). She divides her time between Minneapolis and California where she teaches part time at California State University, Channel Islands.

KATRINA RUTT received an M.A. in creative writing from West Chester University. Her poetry has been set to music and performed at the Kimmel Center for the Performing Arts and the Curtis Institute of Music in Philadelphia. She is an Affiliate Instructor of English at her alma mater, Eastern University.

TOMAŽ ŠALAMUN is widely recognized as one of the leading Central European poets. He lives in Ljubljana and occasionally teaches in the U.S. His recent books translated into English are *The Book for my Brother, Poker, Woods and Chalices, There's the Hand and There's the Arid Chair.* His *Blue Tower* is due out from Houghton Mifflin Harcourt in Spring 2011.

PETER SERCHUK's poems have appeared in a variety of journals big and small, including *Boulevard, Poetry, Denver Quarterly, North American Review, The Texas Review, South Carolina Review, New York Quarterly,* and others. A new collection, *All That Remains,* is just out or will appear shortly from *MARGIE*/Intuit House.

DEBRA SHIRLEY's work has appeared or is forthcoming in *The Cortland Review, MARGIE: The American Journal of Poetry, Main Street Rag, The Adirondack Review,* and the *Playwright's Showcase of the Western Region*. She also recently published *Best Friend on Wheels,* a children's book. Debra is the Director of after-school and summer arts programming at two elementary schools, and teaches writing at the Arvada Center for Arts and Humanities.

JAY SIMMONS has work upcoming in the *Chiron Review,* and has previously published in *Shakespeare's Monkey, Blue Collar Review, Renovation Journal, Pegasus Review, The Quill, Folio, Black Buzzard Review,* and *The Worcester Review.* In 2007, his poem "The Cougar" appeared in *Where the Road Begins,* a tribute to Jack Kerouac on the 50th anniversary of *On the Road.* He lives in New Hampshire and teaches literacy education and writing at the University of Massachusetts, Lowell.

MOHAMAD ATIF SLIM is a new writer from Malaysia. He is presently based in New Zealand, where he is a fourth-year medical student at the University of Auckland. This is his first publication in the U.S.

KAY SLOAN teaches creative writing and American Studies at Miami University of Ohio. She is the author of two novels, a poetry chapbook, and several books on American cultural history. A companion story to "Give Me You" appeared in *Fiction* in 2008.

BRUCE SNIDER is the author of *The Year We Studied Women,* winner of the Felix Pollak Prize in poetry from the University of Wisconsin Press. His poetry has appeared in the *American Poetry Review, Ploughshares, PN Review,* and *Ninth Letter,* among other journals. A former Wallace Stegner Fellow and Jones Lecturer in Poetry at Stanford University, he is the 2010 writer-in-residence at the James Merrill House in Stonington, Connecticut.

Anita Sullivan has two poetry collections, *The Middle Window*, a chapbook (2008), and *Garden of Beasts* (2010). She has published essays and poems in a variety of journals, and holds an M.F.A. in poetry from Pacific Lutheran University in Tacoma, Washington. She lives in Eugene, Oregon.

Marianne Taylor is the recipient of the Allen Ginsberg Award and the Helen A. Quade Memorial Writer's Award, and her manuscript has been a finalist in several major competitions. Her poetry has been published in anthologies and journals such as *North American Review*, *Connecticut Review*, *Alaska Quarterly*, and *Alehouse*. She lives in Mount Vernon, Iowa, and teaches creative writing and literature at Kirkwood Community College.

Mitchell Untch's work has been published in *Los Angeles Review*, *White Pelican Review*, *Third Wednesday*, *Two Hawks Quarterly*, *New Millennium Writers* Contest (Honorable Mention, 2011), and *The Monadnock Anthology* (2011), and was recently chosen as one of six ALOUD Newer Poets, sponsored by the Los Angeles Book Festival, The Mark Taper Forum, and the James Irvine Foundation.

Chris Van Buren currently lives and works in Istanbul. He earned his B.A. from Harvard College in 2008. A former journalist with *The Atlantic* and *News Hour with Jim Lehrer*, he has published poems in *The Harvard Advocate*, *The Gamut*, and *Persephone*.

Debra Wierenga is the author of *Marriage and Other Infidelities*, a poetry chapbook. She lives in Michigan and teaches Creative Writing at Grand Rapids Community College.

Diana Woodcock's forthcoming collection, *Swaying on the Elephant's Shoulders*, won the 2010 Vernice Quebodeaux International Poetry Prize for Women. She has published three chapbooks: *In the Shade of the Sidra Tree* (2010), *Mandala* (2009), and *Travels of a Gwai Lo* (2009). Her poems have appeared in *Best New Poets 2008*, *Nimrod*, *Crab Orchard Review*, *Atlanta Review*, and other journals and anthologies. She currently teaches at Virginia Commonwealth University in Qatar.

# About the Artists

Kathryn Alvarado attended the Prague Summer Program on a photography fellowship in 2006. The photographs in this issue are a small part of that project. Her work has been displayed in galleries in Tucson, Arizona, and Incline Village, Nevada.

Sarah Bienvenu studied art at the Philadelphia College of Art and the Pennsylvania Academy of Fine Arts. In 1979 she settled in New Mexico and emerged as a leading contemporary artist of the Southwest. She is represented in Tulsa by Joseph Gierek Fine Art.

Kimberly Colantino is a photographer who lives in Oregon.

Darren Dirksen is an artist living in Locus Grove, Oklahoma. He is represented in Tulsa by Joseph Gierek Fine Art.

Juan Franco, photographer, is a native of Colombia. He has explored and photographed all over the world, especially South America.

Jen Hoppa graduated from The University of Tulsa. She is a photographer who has taught photography and humanities classes at local colleges.

Kathleen Kemarre is an Australian artist whose work originally appeared in *Nimrod*'s Australia issue.

Martha Kennedy is a Santa Fe-based artist whose art has been exhibited in numerous solo and group exhibitions. She is represented in Tulsa by Joseph Gierek Fine Art.

Erica Lehrer is a poet whose writing appears in this issue. (Full biography on page 189.)

Leslie Ringold is a public defender, poet, and photographer. She lives, works, and plays in Venice, California.

James Andrew Smith attended the Kansas City Art Institute. He worked for ten years as a designer before formally beginning his art career in 2001. His work is exhibited in Tulsa through Joseph Gierek Fine Art.

Roi J. Tamkin is an Atlanta-based photographer and writer. His photographs have appeared in *New Letters, Folio,* and *Nexus*. He contributes articles and photographs to *Skipping Stones Magazine*. He also exhibits his work locally through galleries and alternative spaces.

Mark Weiss, an ophthalmologist in Tulsa, Oklahoma, is an award-winning photographer.